W9-CTQ-691

31

PUBLISHER / EDITOR
Glen R. Serbin

VICE PRESIDENT
Elizabeth Nebb Owen

CONTROLLER
Mai Raack

MARKETING REPRESENTATIVES
Ellie Altomare
Adrian Johnson
Jo Ann Miller
Beth Pierson

DIRECTOR OF PRODUCTION
Tamra Dempsey

PRODUCTION MANAGER
Barbara Kuhn

PRODUCTION STAFF
Terri Wright

PAGE DESIGN SERVICES
Jim Palam & Partners

DISTRIBUTION COORDINATOR
Lynda Lou Moreno

PROOFING
Carey Hobart
Julie Simpson

ACCOUNTING ASSISTANT
Johanna Wagner

MANAGING EDITOR / MAGAZINE DIVISION
Julie Simpson

MANAGER / SITEDESIGNWORKS DIVISION
Christina Henson

SOCIAL MEDIA MARKETING
Iral Zetina

ACCOUNTING FIRM
Damitz, Brooks, Nightingale, Turner & Morrisset

PRINTER
Toppan Printing Co., Ltd.

SHIPPING & MAILING
Express Logistics, Inc.

BOOK DESIGN & ART DIRECTION
David Plunkert / Spur Design

COVER & INTERIOR ILLUSTRATIONS
Paul Blow
pages 610-611
Represented by Anna Goodson
www.agoodson.com

PUBLISHED BY
Serbin Communications, Inc.
813 Reddick Street
Santa Barbara, California 93103
805-963-0439
www.serbin.com
email: info@serbin.com

© 2014 by Serbin Communications, Inc.
All Rights Reserved.

Directory of Illustration is a trademark of Serbin Communications, Inc.

Copyright under International and Pan-American Copyright Convention. Printed in Hong Kong.

No part of this book may be reproduced, stored in a retrieval system, or transmitted in any form, or by any means, electronic, mechanical, photocopying, recording or otherwise, without the prior permission of the publisher.

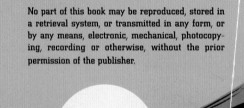

Aa

Bb

Cc

Comm. for IFC.

Comm. by Men's Health Magazine.

Comm. by British Airway's High Life Magazine.

Comm. by Glamour Magazine.

James Taylor

début **art** • Illustrators, Photographers and Fine Artists Agents
30 Tottenham Street, London, W1T 4RJ. United Kingdom
Tel: 01144 20 7636 1064. email: **info@debutart.com**
The Coningsby Gallery • Tel: 01144 20 7636 7478

www.debutart.com • **www.twitter.com/debutart**

début **art**

début **art** • Illustrators, Photographers and Fine Artists Agents
30 Tottenham Street, London, W1T 4RJ. United Kingdom
London • Tel: +44 (0)20 7636 1064. **New York** • Tel: 212 995 5044
email: **info@debutart.com** • **www.debutart.com**
London • New York • Berlin

Since 1985, *début* **art** (based in London, England and now with offices in New York and Paris) has proactively sought out leading contemporary image-makers & clients who create original, progressive and commercially successful media material. Today, *début* **art** and the highly artistic illustrators it promotes, are widely regarded, both in the UK and around the world, as representing one of the finest and most contemporary talent groupings in the field of illustration.

début **art** and the illustrators it markets have successfully undertaken assignments worldwide for very many companies that are leaders in their fields including: Microsoft, Apple, Coca-Cola, Proctor and Gamble, Samsung, Levi's, Nokia, Rolls-Royce, BP, Shell, Nike, The Chicago Mercantile Exchange, The NYSE, The London Stock Exchange, Bloomberg, American Express, Barclaycard, HSBC, IBM, British Airways, Unilever, Harrods, Selfridges, Macy's (New York), McDonalds Topshop, Verizon, Lucas Inc, The Royal Opera House (London), Universal Music, Sony, Miller, Burton, Harper Collins, The Wall Street Journal, The New York Times, The Times (London), Le Monde, The Economist, The Financial Times, Vogue, Cosmopolitan and National Geographic Magazine.

Full portfolios for every artist can be reviewed and requested via our web site at **www.debutart.com**

The Coningsby Gallery stages some 30 exhibitions per year by selected leading illustrators, photographers and fine artists. Review of previous exhibitions, a look at upcoming shows and a photo tour of the gallery itself can be accessed at **www.coningsbygallery.com**

Contact: Andrew Coningsby, Jonathan Hedley, Rhiannon Lloyd, Mimi Rich, Holly Lloyd, Robert Saxon & Cezanne Noordhoek.

Kid Acne	Peter Crowther	Nanette Hoogslag	Chris Labrooy	Chris Price	Jim Tsinganos
Alan Aldridge	Marta Cerda	Sarah Howell	Yann Legendre	Paul Price	Stephen Vuillemin
Arno	Matthew Dartford	Frazer Hudson	Andy Lovell	Peter Quinnell	Stephanie von Reiswitz
Andrew Baker	Paul Davis	Drawn Ideas	Harry Malt	Steve Rawlings	Jeff Wack
Istvan Banyai	Carol del Angel	ilovedust	Stephane Manel	Nick Reddyhoff	Kevin Waldron
Gary Bates	Pierre Doucin	Infomen	Sophie Marsham	The Red Dress	Stephan Walter
Kathrin Baxter	Barry Downard	Jacey	Kim McGillivray	Redseal	Neil Webb
Jon Berkeley	Katie Edwards	JaceyTec	Vince McIndoe	Cath Riley	Jane Webster
Chris Bianchi	El Señor	Jackdaw	Wesley Merritt	Craig Robinson	Louise Weir
Borja	Tim Ellis	Ben Jennings	Justin Metz	Kerry Roper	Joe Wilson
Jacquie Boyd	Kilian Eng	Hans Jenssen	MinaLima	Saeko	Oscar Wilson
Norm Breyfogle	Sam Falconer	Ben Johnston	Gabriel Moreno	Craig Shuttlewood	Alex Williamson
Jon Burgerman	Helen Friel	Sarah Jones	Patrick Morgan	Peter Strain	Tina Zellmer
Oliver Burston	Dan Funderburgh	Sam Kerr	Morten Morland	Michel Streich	Jurgen Ziewe
Benedict Campbell	Patrick George	Alan Kitching	Huntley/Muir	Sroop Sunar	Vasili Zorin
Danny Capozzi	Peter Grundy	Ronald Kurniawan	Neasden Control Ctr	Tado	
James Carey	Sarah Hanson	Christina K	Walter Newton	James Taylor	
Celyn	Jethro Haynes	Nik Keevil	Chris Nurse	Yehrin Tong	
Tracie Ching	Matt Herring	Yuko Kondo	Alex Pang	Sophie Toulouse	
Russell Cobb	Oliver Hibert	Kolchoz	Paper Work	Dominic Trevett	
Matthew Cooper	hitandrun	La Boca	Pietari Posti	Alex Trochut	

'**Beauty is truth, truth beauty**'
John Keats

011

Comm. for Virgin Media.

Comm. by Fast Company Magazine.

Comm. by Readers Digest Magazine.

Comm. by Nike.

Chris Labrooy

début **art** • Illustrators, Photographers and Fine Artists Agents
30 Tottenham Street, London, W1T 4RJ. United Kingdom
Tel: 01144 20 7636 1064. email: **info@debutart.com**
The Coningsby Gallery • Tel: 01144 20 7636 7478

www.debutart.com • **www.twitter.com/debutart**

NIKE AIR MAX 90 SNEAKERBOOT
LOCATION : LONDON

Comm. by Nike.

Comm. by IEEE Spectrum Magazine.

Comm. by Transport For London.

Self-initiated.

Self-initiated.

Comm. by The City Paper.

Comm. by Philadelphia Magazine.

Gabriel Moreno

début **art** • Illustrators, Photographers and Fine Artists Agents
30 Tottenham Street, London, W1T 4RJ. United Kingdom
Tel: 01144 20 7636 1064. email: **info@debutart.com**
The Coningsby Gallery • Tel: 01144 20 7636 7478

www.debutart.com • **www.twitter.com/debutart**

Comm. Mahou Premium Light.

Self-initiated.

Comm. for Vodka Cruiser.

Comm. for Southern Railway.

début art

Comm. by The Rockefeller Institute.

Comm. by Financial Times.

Comm. for Telos.

Andrew Baker

début **art** • Illustrators, Photographers and Fine Artists Agents
30 Tottenham Street, London, W1T 4RJ. United Kingdom
Tel: 01144 20 7636 1064. email: **info@debutart.com**
The Coningsby Gallery • Tel: 01144 20 7636 7478

www.debutart.com • **www.twitter.com/debutart**

début **art**

The Economist

SPECIAL REPORT
CHINA AND THE INTERNET
April 6th 2013

A giant cage

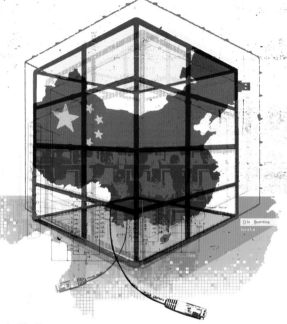

Comm. by The Economist Magazine.

Comm. by Bloomberg Businessweek Magazine.

Comm. by Wall St Journal..

Alex Williamson

début **art** • Illustrators, Photographers and Fine Artists Agents
30 Tottenham Street, London, W1T 4RJ. United Kingdom
Tel: 01144 20 7636 1064.   email: **info@debutart.com**
The Coningsby Gallery • Tel: 01144 20 7636 7478

www.debutart.com • **www.twitter.com/debutart**

début **art**

Self-initiated.

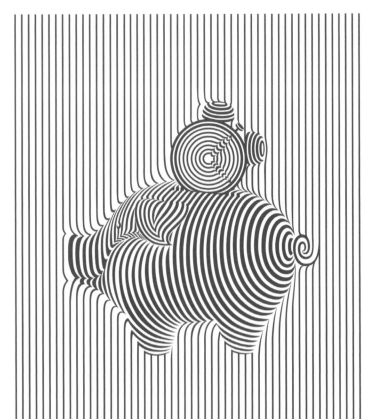

Comm. for Penstripe. Comm. by Taxi Studio

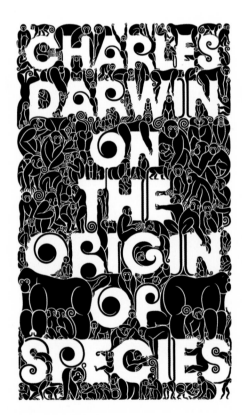

Comm. by White's Books.

Comm. by Bloomberg Businessweek.

Yehrin Tong

début **art** • Illustrators, Photographers and Fine Artists Agents
30 Tottenham Street, London, W1T 4RJ. United Kingdom
Tel: 01144 20 7636 1064. email: **info@debutart.com**
The Coningsby Gallery • Tel: 01144 20 7636 7478

www.debutart.com • www.twitter.com/debutart

Comm. for Penstripe. Comm. by Taxi Studio

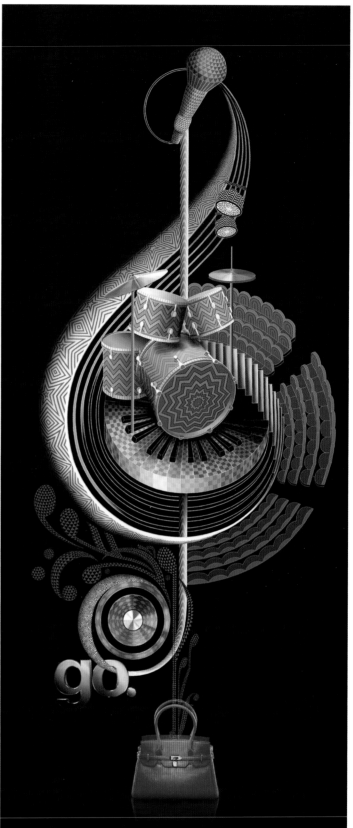

Comm. by New Scientist Magazine.

Comm. by Visa.

Comm. by Atlanta Magazine.

Comm. by J Magazine.

Comm. by Men's Fitness Magazine.

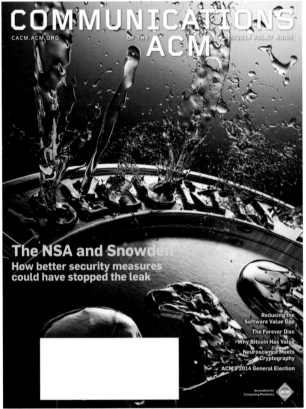

Comm. by Communications ACM Magazine.

Peter Crowther Associates

début **art** • Illustrators, Photographers and Fine Artists Agents
30 Tottenham Street, London, W1T 4RJ. United Kingdom
Tel: 01144 20 7636 1064. email: **info@debutart.com**
The Coningsby Gallery • Tel: 01144 20 7636 7478

www.debutart.com • www.twitter.com/debutart

Comm. by Mazda Magazine.

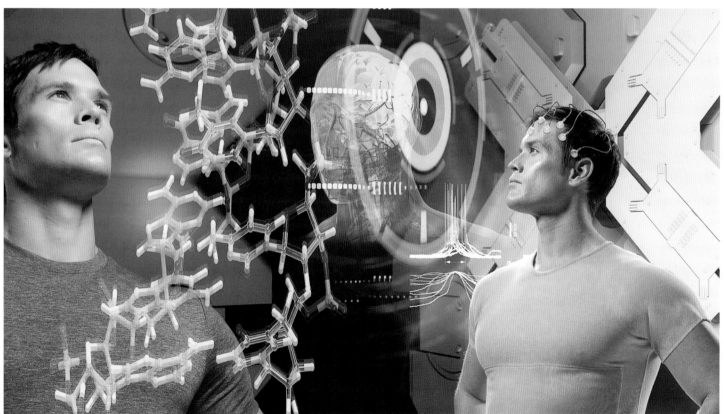

Comm. by Men's Health Magazine.

début art

Comm. by Men's Health Magazine.

Comm. by the Washingtonian.

Comm. by Zip Design.

Comm. by Runner's World Magazine

Peter Crowther Associates

début **art** • Illustrators, Photographers and Fine Artists Agents
30 Tottenham Street, London, W1T 4RJ. United Kingdom
Tel: 01144 20 7636 1064. email: **info@debutart.com**
The Coningsby Gallery • Tel: 01144 20 7636 7478

www.debutart.com • www.twitter.com/debutart

Comm. by Time Out London.

Comm. for Cornell Enterprise Magazine.

Comm. by Men's Health Magazine.

début **art**

Comm. for Red Bull.

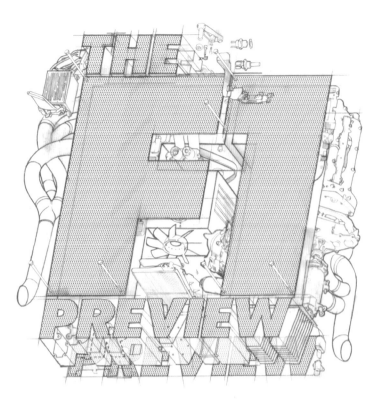

Comm. by Gulf Life Magazine.

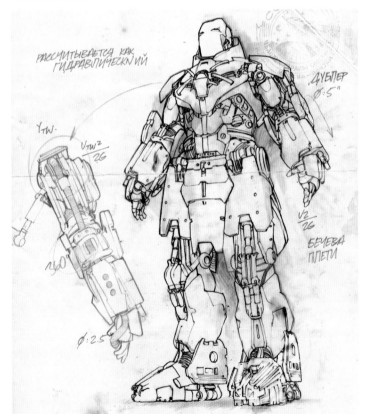

Comm. by Insight Editions.

Self-initiated.

James Carey

*déb: *art* • Illustrators, Photographers and Fine Artists Agents
30 Tottenham Street, London, W1T 4RJ. United Kingdom
Tel: 01144 20 7636 1064. email: **info@debutart.com**
The Coningsby Gallery • Tel: 01144 20 7636 7478

www.debutart.com • **www.twitter.com/debutart**

Comm. by Hachette.

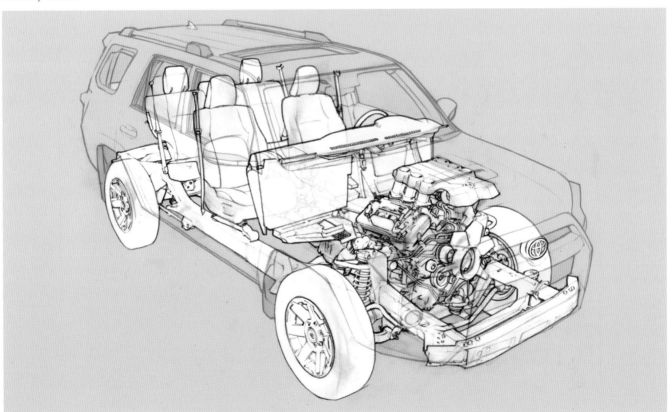

Comm. for Toyota 4Runner.

début **art**

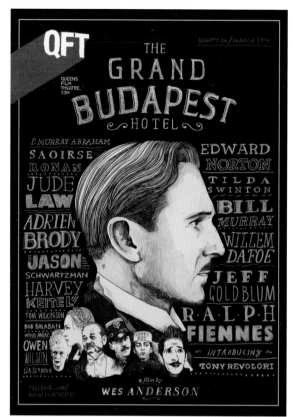

Comm. by QFT Cinema.

Self-initiated.

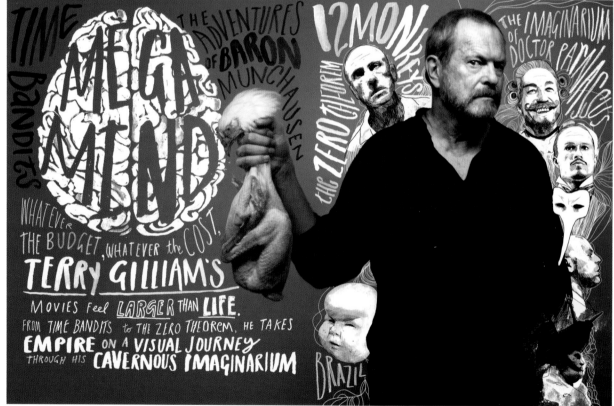

Comm. by Empire Magazine.

Peter Strain

début **art** • Illustrators, Photographers and Fine Artists Agents
30 Tottenham Street, London, W1T 4RJ. United Kingdom
Tel: 01144 20 7636 1064. email: **info@debutart.com**
The Coningsby Gallery • Tel: 01144 20 7636 7478

www.debutart.com • www.twitter.com/debutart

début art

Comm. by Dash Magazine.

Pierre Cardin. Comm. by The FT.

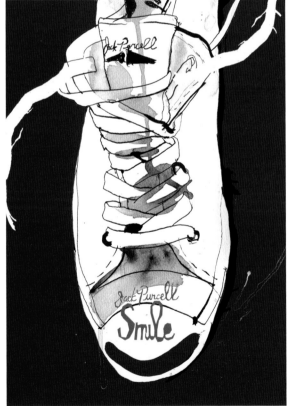

Comm. by Converse.

Comm. Self-initiated.

Patrick Morgan

début **art** • Illustrators, Photographers and Fine Artists Agents
30 Tottenham Street, London, W1T 4RJ. United Kingdom
Tel: 01144 20 7636 1064. email: **info@debutart.com**
The Coningsby Gallery • Tel: 01144 20 7636 7478

www.debutart.com • www.twitter.com/debutart

début art

Comm. by Ted Baker Eyewear.

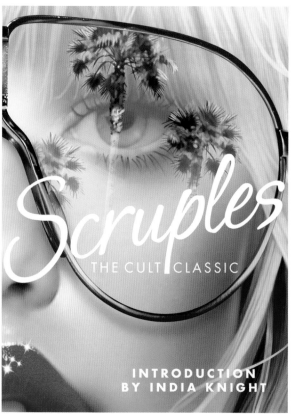

Comm. by Little Brown Book Group.

Comm. by Hed Kandi.

Self-initiated.

Arn0

début art • Illustrators, Photographers and Fine Artists Agents
30 Tottenham Street, London, W1T 4RJ. United Kingdom
Tel: 01144 20 7636 1064. email: **info@debutart.com**
The Coningsby Gallery • Tel: 01144 20 7636 7478

www.debutart.com • **www.twitter.com/debutart**

début **art**

Private Commission.

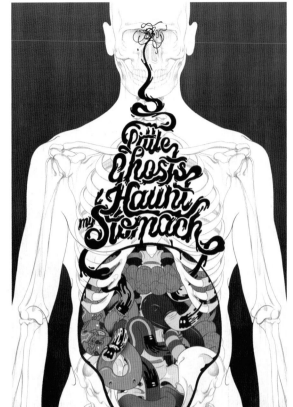

Comm. by Watson DG.

Comm. by Shop Magazine.

Comm. by Intelligent Life Magazine.

Andrew Archer

début **art** • Illustrators, Photographers and Fine Artists Agents
30 Tottenham Street, London, W1T 4RJ. United Kingdom
Tel: 01144 20 7636 1064. email: **info@debutart.com**
The Coningsby Gallery • Tel: 01144 20 7636 7478

www.debutart.com • www.twitter.com/debutart

début **art**

029

Comm. for NatWest Bank.

Comm. by Wall St Journal.

Comm. for New York Lottery.

Matthew Dartford / Flip CG

début **art** • Illustrators, Photographers and Fine Artists Agents
30 Tottenham Street, London, W1T 4RJ. United Kingdom
Tel: 01144 20 7636 1064. email: **info@debutart.com**
The Coningsby Gallery • Tel: 01144 20 7636 7478

www.debutart.com • **www.twitter.com/debutart**

Comm. by Which? Magazine.

Comm. for Ribena

More wide-aisle gates

We've introduced wide-aisle gates at most of London Overground and Tube stations to provide easier access for wheelchair users, assistance-dog owners, people with buggies and passengers with luggage. This is just one of the ways we reinvest all our income to run and improve your services.

Comm. by Transport For London.

Comm. for Wrigley.

début art

Comm. for Adidas.

Comm. by Harvill Secker Publishing.

Comm. for HBO.

Joe Wilson

début **art** • Illustrators, Photographers and Fine Artists Agents
30 Tottenham Street, London, W1T 4RJ. United Kingdom
Tel: 01144 20 7636 1064. email: **info@debutart.com**
The Coningsby Gallery • Tel: 01144 20 7636 7478

www.debutart.com • **www.twitter.com/debutart**

Comm. by Walker Books.

Comm. for London Fashion Week.

Self-initiated.

Comm. by EMI.

Comm. by New Scientist Magazine.

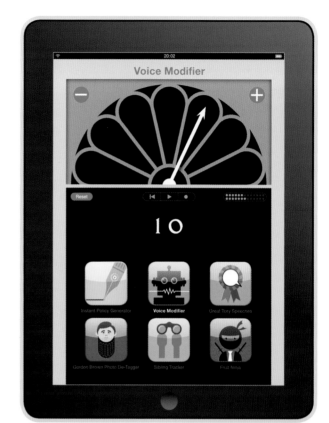

Comm. by GQ Magazine.

Comm. by Salon du Vintage.

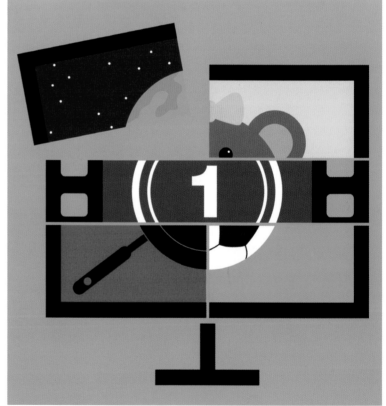

Comm. for Invitel.

Patrick George

début **art** • Illustrators, Photographers and Fine Artists Agents
30 Tottenham Street, London, W1T 4RJ. United Kingdom
Tel: 01144 20 7636 1064. email: **info@debutart.com**
The Coningsby Gallery • Tel: 01144 20 7636 7478

www.debutart.com • **www.twitter.com/debutart**

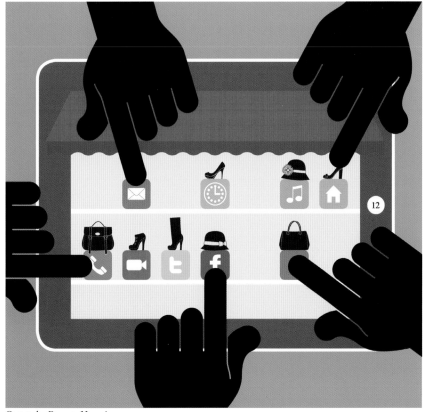

Comm. by Drapers Magazine.

Comm. by Kiplinger's Personal Finance Magazine.

Comm. by The London Magazine.

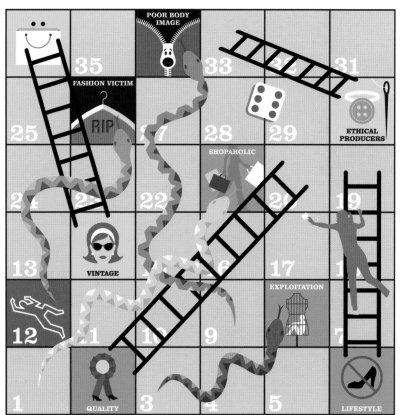

Comm. by The Wall Street Journal.

Comm. for i3 Magazine.

Comm. by Director Magazine.

Comm. for LA Motor Show.

Jackdaw

début **art** • Illustrators, Photographers and Fine Artists Agents
30 Tottenham Street, London, W1T 4RJ. United Kingdom
Tel: 01144 20 7636 1064. email: **info@debutart.com**
The Coningsby Gallery • Tel: 01144 20 7636 7478

www.debutart.com • www.twitter.com/debutart

début **art**

Comm. for Best Western Magazine.

Comm. for Ryanair Let's Go Magazine.

Comm. for Barclaycard.

Matt Herring

début **art** • Illustrators, Photographers and Fine Artists Agents
30 Tottenham Street, London, W1T 4RJ. United Kingdom
Tel: 01144 20 7636 1064. email: **info@debutart.com**
The Coningsby Gallery • Tel: 01144 20 7636 7478

www.debutart.com • **www.twitter.com/debutart**

début **art**

Comm. by ACM Magazine.

Comm. by Men's Fitness Magazine.

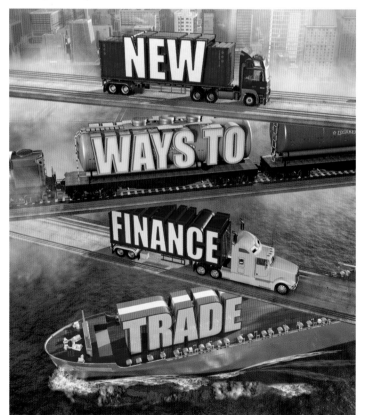
Comm. by The Banker Magazine.

Comm. by ACM Magazine.

Barry Downard

début **art** • Illustrators, Photographers and Fine Artists Agents
30 Tottenham Street, London, W1T 4RJ. United Kingdom
Tel: 01144 20 7636 1064. email: **info@debutart.com**
The Coningsby Gallery • Tel: 01144 20 7636 7478

www.debutart.com • www.twitter.com/debutart

début **art**

PAM GRIER is
Foxy Brown
SHE'S THE MEANEST CHICK IN TOWN!

Comm. by Arrow Films.

Comm. by Bloomsbury Books.

Comm. by Ted Baker Eyewear.

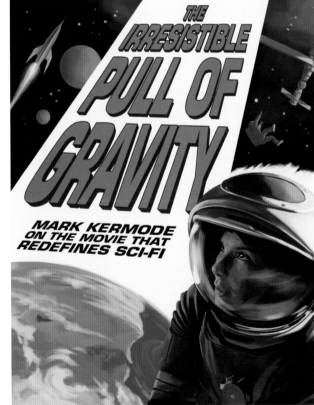

Comm. by British Airways High Life Magazine.

The Red Dress

début **art** • Illustrators, Photographers and Fine Artists Agents
30 Tottenham Street, London, W1T 4RJ. United Kingdom
Tel: 01144 20 7636 1064. email: info@debutart.com
The Coningsby Gallery • Tel: 01144 20 7636 7478

www.debutart.com • www.twitter.com/debutart

début **art**

Comm. for RICS' Modus Magazine.

Comm. by Technology Review Magazine.

Self-initiated.

Nick Reddyhoff

début **art** • Illustrators, Photographers and Fine Artists Agents
30 Tottenham Street, London, W1T 4RJ. United Kingdom
Tel: 01144 20 7636 1064. email: **info@debutart.com**
The Coningsby Gallery • Tel: 01144 20 7636 7478

www.debutart.com • **www.twitter.com/debutart**

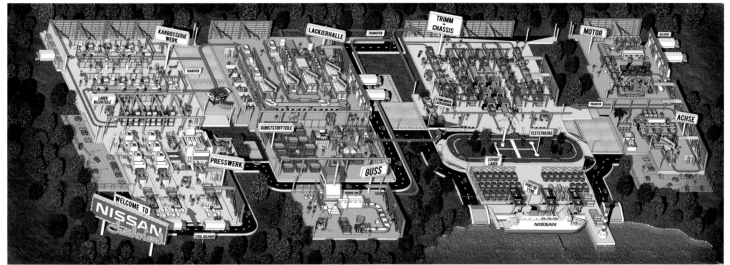

Comm. for Nissan.

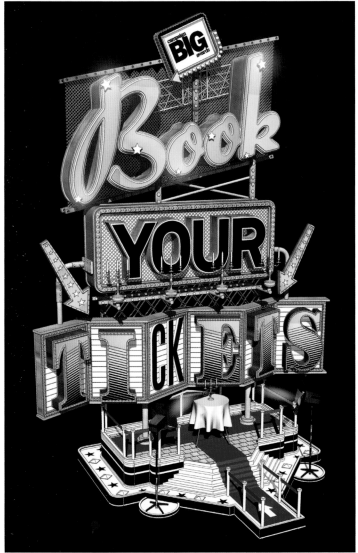

Comm. for Campaign Magazine's Big Awards

Comm. by LA Times.

Stephan Walter

début **art** • Illustrators, Photographers and Fine Artists Agents
30 Tottenham Street, London, W1T 4RJ. United Kingdom
Tel: 01144 20 7636 1064. email: **info@debutart.com**
The Coningsby Gallery • Tel: 01144 20 7636 7478

www.debutart.com • **www.twitter.com/debutart**

début **art**

"Most people see a tee shot. I see kinetics and energy transfer from club to ball."

Chevron is proud to help inspire kids by supporting Science, Technology, Engineering and Math (STEM) education.

We partner with organizations such as Project Lead The Way, which helps bring STEM curricula to 400,000 students.

chevron.com/education

Chevron
Human Energy

CHEVRON, the CHEVRON Hallmark and HUMAN ENERGY are registered trademarks of Chevron Intellectual Property LLC. © 2013 Chevron U.S.A. Inc. All rights reserved.

Comm. for Chevron.

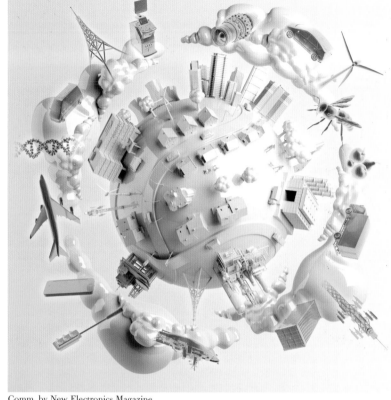

Comm. by New Electronics Magazine.

Comm. by Investor's Chronicle Magazine.

Comm. by Investor's Chronicle Magazine.

Oliver Burtson

début **art** • Illustrators, Photographers and Fine Artists Agents
30 Tottenham Street, London, W1T 4RJ. United Kingdom
Tel: 01144 20 7636 1064. email: **info@debutart.com**
The Coningsby Gallery • Tel: 01144 20 7636 7478

www.debutart.com • **www.twitter.com/debutart**

début **art**

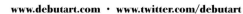

Comm. by Eurostar Metropolitan Magazine.

Comm. by Ryanair's Let's Go Magazine.

Comm. by Fast Company Magazine.

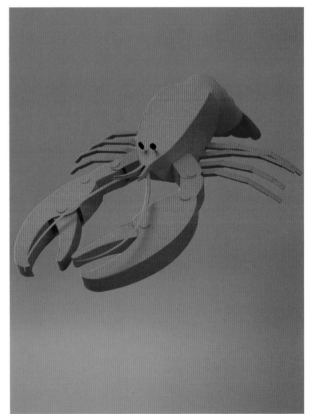

Comm. by Ted Baker Clothing C.o.

Helen Friel

début **art** • Illustrators, Photographers and Fine Artists Agents
30 Tottenham Street, London, W1T 4RJ. United Kingdom
Tel: 01144 20 7636 1064. email: **info@debutart.com**
The Coningsby Gallery • Tel: 01144 20 7636 7478

www.debutart.com • **www.twitter.com/debutart**

début **art**

Comm. by Air France Magazine.

Comm. by Luxury Travel Magazine.

Comm. for Withers Worldwide.

Neil Webb

début **art** • Illustrators, Photographers and Fine Artists Agents
30 Tottenham Street, London, W1T 4RJ. United Kingdom
Tel: 01144 20 7636 1064. email: **info@debutart.com**
The Coningsby Gallery • Tel: 01144 20 7636 7478

www.debutart.com • **www.twitter.com/debutart**

Comm. by New York Times.

Comm. by Which? Magazine.

Comm. by Springboard Magazine.

début **art**

Kilian Eng. Private Commission.

Kilian Eng. Private Commission.

Matthew Cooper. Comm. by Domino Records.

Matthew Cooper. Comm. by EMI Production Music.

début **art** • Illustrators, Photographers and Fine Artists Agents
30 Tottenham Street, London, W1T 4RJ. United Kingdom
Tel: 01144 20 7636 1064. email: **info@debutart.com**
The Coningsby Gallery • Tel: 01144 20 7636 7478

www.debutart.com • **www.twitter.com/debutart**

début **art**

Self-initiated.

Comm. by The National Trust Of Scotland

Comm. for Romana Sambvca.

Comm. for The Ross Poster Group.

Vince McIndoe

début **art** • Illustrators, Photographers and Fine Artists Agents
30 Tottenham Street, London, W1T 4RJ. United Kingdom
Tel: 01144 20 7636 1064. email: **info@debutart.com**
The Coningsby Gallery • Tel: 01144 20 7636 7478

www.debutart.com • **www.twitter.com/debutart**

début **art**

Oscar Wilson. Comm. by Cannongate Books.

Banking can be a tricky subject. So our goal is to make sure everyone understands a bit more about the complex world of money and we'll do whatever we can to cut through the bafflement. That could be educating schoolkids about the value of money with our Make £5 Grow scheme, or working with The Times to create supplements like this one. You see, we think banking's better when we're all on the same page.

Let us tell you more at virginmoney.com

On a quest to make banking better

Oscar Wilson. Comm. for Virgin Bank.

Sarah Hanson. Comm. by Random House.

Sarah Hanson. Comm. by Benefits Selling Magazine.

début **art** • Illustrators, Photographers and Fine Artists Agents
30 Tottenham Street, London, W1T 4RJ. United Kingdom
Tel: 01144 20 7636 1064. email: **info@debutart.com**
The Coningsby Gallery • Tel: 01144 20 7636 7478

www.debutart.com • **www.twitter.com/debutart**

048

Ceci n'est pas un Belge

Comm. by The Daily Telegraph.

Comm. by The Daily Telegraph.

VOTE RASCAL!

Comm. by The Daily Telegraph.

Comm. by RSA Journal.

Wesley Merritt

début **art** • Illustrators, Photographers and Fine Artists Agents
30 Tottenham Street, London, W1T 4RJ. United Kingdom
Tel: 01144 20 7636 1064. email: **info@debutart.com**
The Coningsby Gallery • Tel: 01144 20 7636 7478

www.debutart.com • **www.twitter.com/debutart**

début **art**

Tado. Comm. by Xbox.

Tado. Comm. by Xbox.

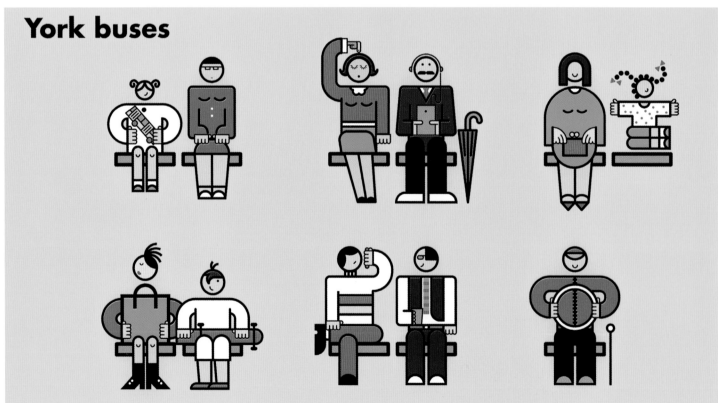

York buses

Peter Grundy. Comm. for the City of York.

début **art** • Illustrators, Photographers and Fine Artists Agents
30 Tottenham Street, London, W1T 4RJ. United Kingdom
Tel: 01144 20 7636 1064. email: **info@debutart.com**
The Coningsby Gallery • Tel: 01144 20 7636 7478

www.debutart.com • **www.twitter.com/debutart**

début **art**

Comm. for Union Postale Magazine.

Comm. by Quality World Magazine.

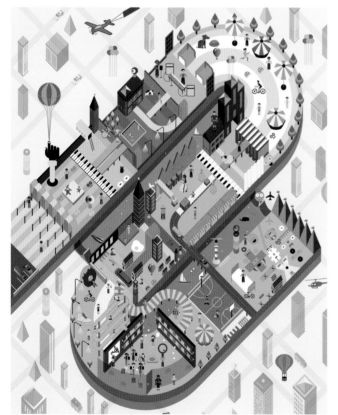

Comm. by The Kaiser Oakland Hospital.

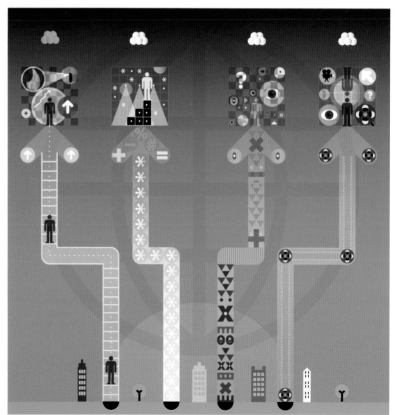

Comm. by Harvard Business Review.

Infomen

début **art** • Illustrators, Photographers and Fine Artists Agents
30 Tottenham Street, London, W1T 4RJ. United Kingdom
Tel: 01144 20 7636 1064. email: **info@debutart.com**
The Coningsby Gallery • Tel: 01144 20 7636 7478

www.debutart.com • **www.twitter.com/debutart**

début **art**

Celyn. Comm. for Macmillan Cancer Care.

Celyn. Comm. by Lush.

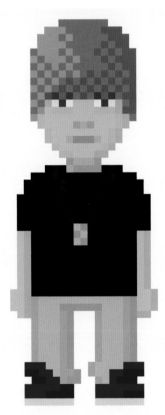

Craig Robinson. Self-initiated.

Craig Robinson. Self-initiated.

début **art** • Illustrators, Photographers and Fine Artists Agents
30 Tottenham Street, London, W1T 4RJ. United Kingdom
Tel: 01144 20 7636 1064. email: **info@debutart.com**
The Coningsby Gallery • Tel: 01144 20 7636 7478

www.debutart.com • www.twitter.com/debutart

début **art**

Comm. by Fortune Magazine.

Self-initiated.

Self-initiated

Patrick Vale

début **art** • Illustrators, Photographers and Fine Artists Agents
30 Tottenham Street, London, W1T 4RJ. United Kingdom
Tel: 01144 20 7636 1064. email: **info@debutart.com**
The Coningsby Gallery • Tel: 01144 20 7636 7478

www.debutart.com • www.twitter.com/debutart

début **art**

Comm. by Livingstone Partners.

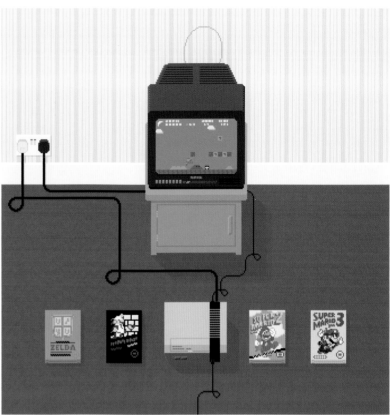
Self-initiated.

Self-initiated.

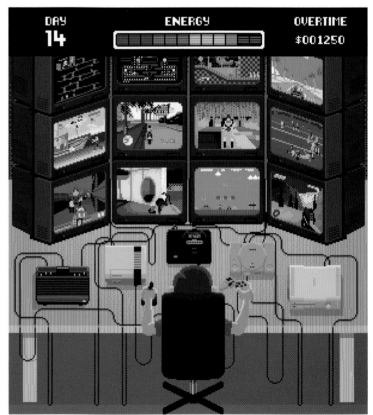
Comm. by Maxim Magazine.

Walter Newton

début **art** • Illustrators, Photographers and Fine Artists Agents
30 Tottenham Street, London, W1T 4RJ. United Kingdom
Tel: 01144 20 7636 1064. email: **info@debutart.com**
The Coningsby Gallery • Tel: 01144 20 7636 7478

www.debutart.com • **www.twitter.com/debutart**

début **art**

Comm. for Axe.

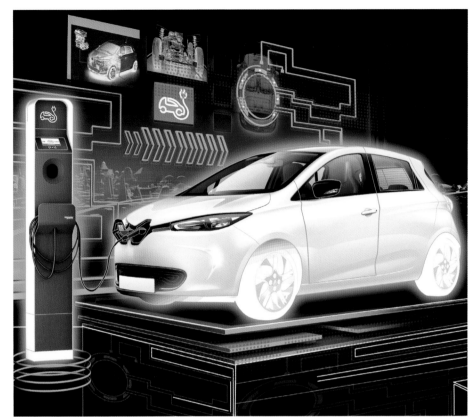

Comm. by BBC Top Gear Magazine.

Comm. by Harper Collins/

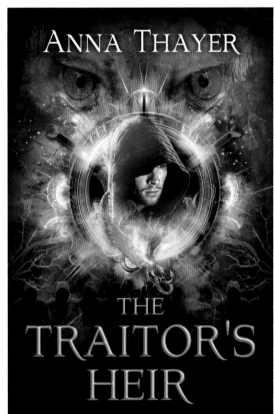

Comm. by Lion Hudson.

Jacey

début **art** • Illustrators, Photographers and Fine Artists Agents
30 Tottenham Street, London, W1T 4RJ. United Kingdom
Tel: 01144 20 7636 1064.   email: **info@debutart.com**
The Coningsby Gallery • Tel: 01144 20 7636 7478

www.debutart.com • www.twitter.com/debutart

début **art**

Comm. for TIME Magazine.

Comm. byMidwives Magazine.

Comm. by Empire Magazine.

Justin Metz

début **art** • Illustrators, Photographers and Fine Artists Agents
30 Tottenham Street, London, W1T 4RJ. United Kingdom
Tel: 01144 20 7636 1064.   email: **info@debutart.com**
The Coningsby Gallery • Tel: 01144 20 7636 7478

www.debutart.com • **www.twitter.com/debutart**

ros. Ent. All Rights Reserved

Comm. by Warner Bros.

Comm. by Quality World Magazine.

Comm. by for Sky Broadcasting.

début **art**

Comm. for Cole Haan.

Comm. for The Oosten Williamsburg

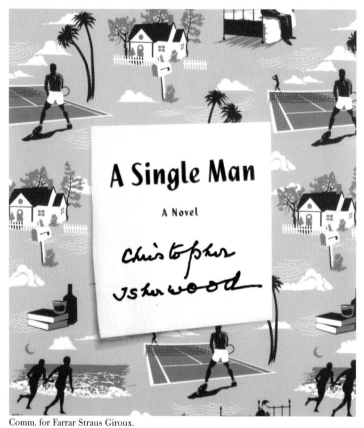

Comm. for Farrar Straus Giroux.

Comm. for Microsoft.

Dan Funderburgh

début **art** • Illustrators, Photographers and Fine Artists Agents
30 Tottenham Street, London, W1T 4RJ. United Kingdom
Tel: 01144 20 7636 1064. email: **info@debutart.com**
The Coningsby Gallery • Tel: 01144 20 7636 7478

www.DEBUTART.com • www.twitter.com/debutart

début **art**

SHANNON ASSOCIATES

212 333 2551   SHANNONASSOCIATES.COM

NICOLAS DELORT

SHANNON ASSOCIATES
212.333.2551

DEJA VU

Eyewear Inspired!

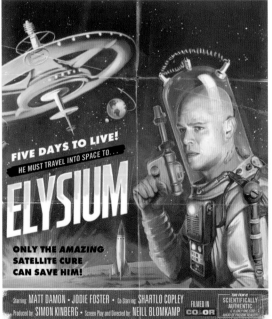

FIVE DAYS TO LIVE!
HE MUST TRAVEL INTO SPACE TO...

ELYSIUM

ONLY THE AMAZING
SATELLITE CURE
CAN SAVE HIM!

Starring: MATT DAMON · JODIE FOSTER · Co-Starring: SHARTLO COPLEY · FILMED IN COLOR
Produced by: SIMON KINBERG · Screen Play and Directed by: NEILL BLOMKAMP

THIS FILM IS SCIENTIFICALLY AUTHENTIC IT IS ONLY ONE STEP AHEAD OF PRESENT REALITY!

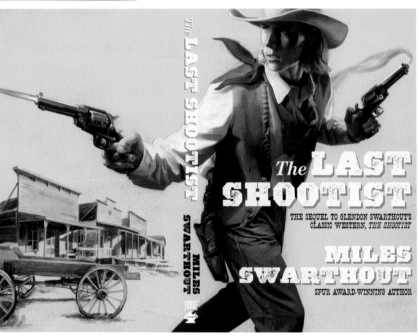

The LAST SHOOTIST

The LAST SHOOTIST

THE SEQUEL TO GLENDON SWARTHOUT'S
CLASSIC WESTERN, *THE SHOOTIST*

MILES SWARTHOUT

MILES SWARTHOUT
SPUR AWARD-WINNING AUTHOR

Forge

shannonassociates.com

SHANNON ASSOCIATES
212.333.2551

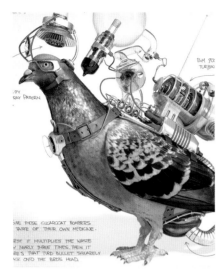

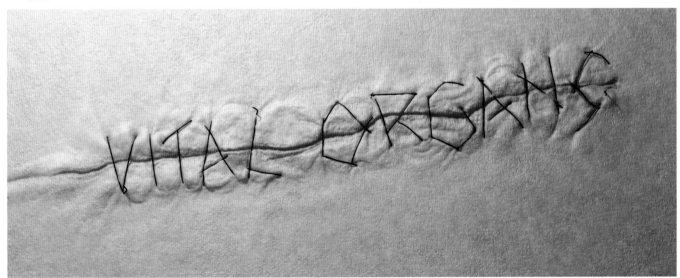

SHANNON ASSOCIATES
212.333.2551

SHANNON ASSOCIATES
212.333.2551

SHANNON ASSOCIATES
212.333.2551

shannonassociates.com

SHANNON ASSOCIATES
212.333.2551

CHRIS COCOZZA

SHANNON ASSOCIATES
212.333.2551

SHANNON ASSOCIATES
212.333.2551

SHANNON ASSOCIATES
212.333.2551

SHANNON ASSOCIATES
212.333.2551

SHANNON ASSOCIATES
212.333.2551

shannonassociates.com

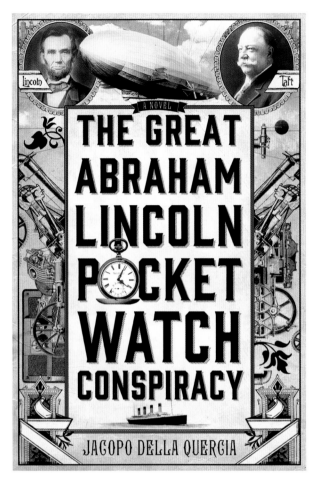

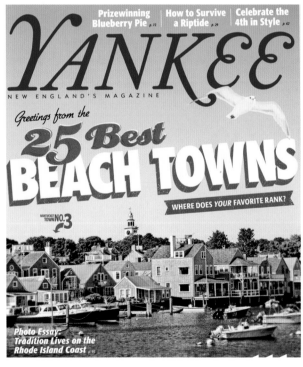

SHANNON ASSOCIATES
212.333.2551

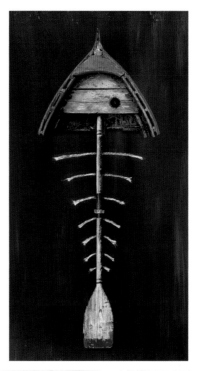

SHANNON ASSOCIATES
212.333.2551

SHANNON ASSOCIATES
212.333.2551

shannonassociates.com

shannonassociates.com

(Clockwise from top left)
Uma Thurman in *Kill Bill—
Vol. 1*; Charles Bronson

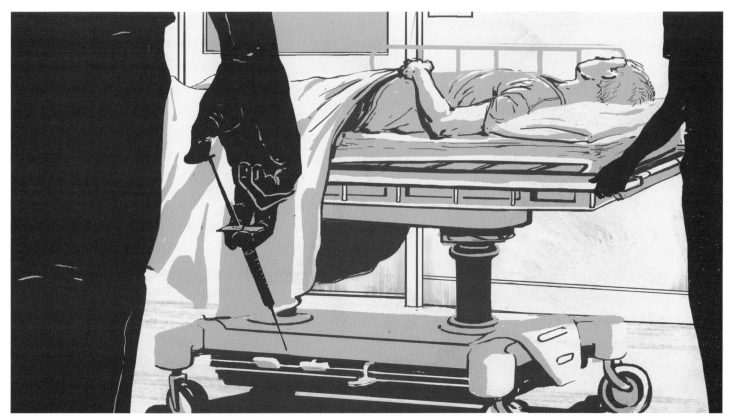

SHANNON ASSOCIATES
212.333.2551

DOYLE & DOYLE
J E W E L E R S

412 W 13TH STREET | NEW YORK, NY 10014 | WWW.DOYLEDOYLE.COM | 212.677.9991

SHANNON ASSOCIATES
212.333.2551

CHOCOLATE ORANGE FUDGE

2½ cups semisweet chocolate chips
1 (14 ounce) can sweetened condensed milk
½ teaspoon orange extract • 2 teaspoons orange zest

Line an 8x8 inch square pan with parchment paper.
Melt chocolate chips with condensed milk. Stir until
smooth. Remove from heat and stir in zest and extract.
Pour chocolate mixture into pan. Chill for two hours or
until firm and cut into squares. Share with your sweetie!

ALFR. NOBEL

Katy K's
The Frothy Monkey
MODA
Imogene + Willie
The Filling Station
Burger Up
Halcyon Bike Shop
Las Paletas

BEECHWOOD AVE.
15TH AVE.
SWEETBRIAR AVE.
MONTROSE AVE.
DALLAS AVE.
HALCYON AVE.
PARIS AVE.
12TH AVENUE SOUTH

12 South

SHANNON ASSOCIATES
212.333.2551

SHANNON ASSOCIATES
212.333.2551

THE NIGHT TIDE

SHANNON ASSOCIATES
212.333.2551

viral
nation

shaunta grimes

SHANNON ASSOCIATES
212.333.2551

SHANNON ASSOCIATES
212.333.2551

SHANNON ASSOCIATES
212.333.2551

SHANNON ASSOCIATES
212.333.2551

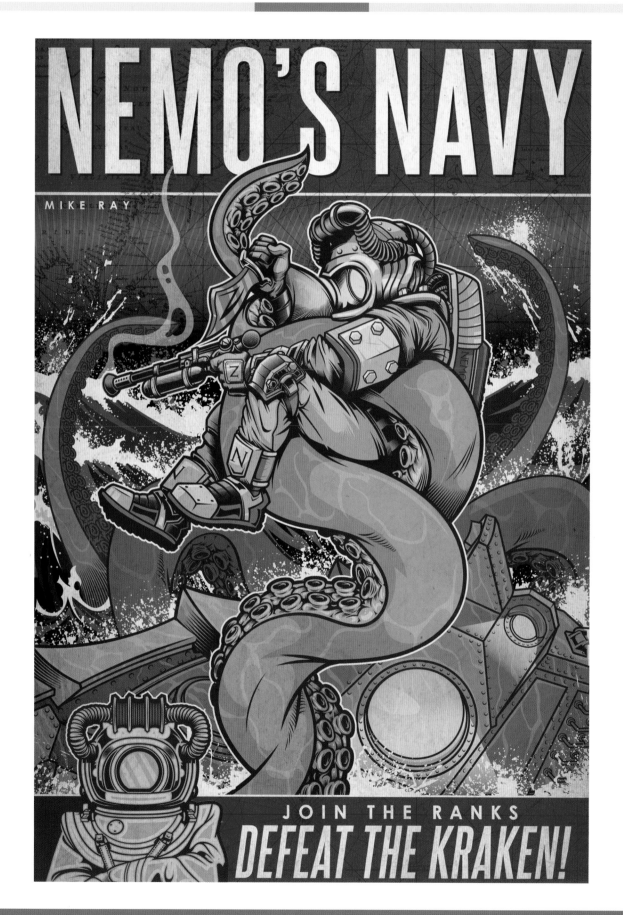

shannonassociates.com

SHANNON ASSOCIATES
212.333.2551

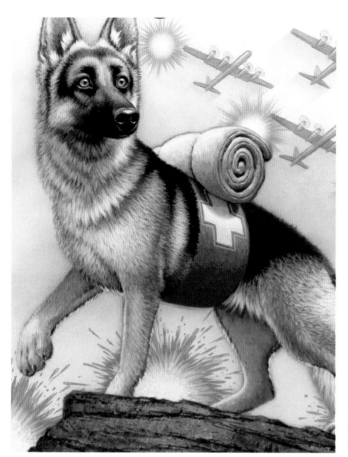

SHANNON ASSOCIATES
212.333.2551

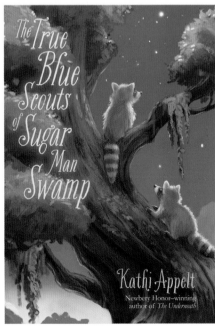

VALERIO FABBRETTI

SHANNON ASSOCIATES
212.333.2551

DELORT **ELWELL** **FARICY** **JAMES**

MARCONI **ST.PIERRE** **PETERSON** **PROCTOR**

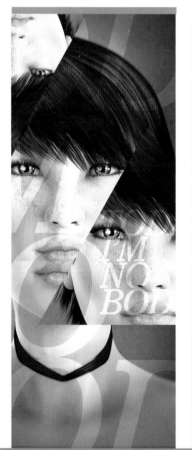

shannonassociates.com

RODWELL   GABOR   MACIEL   KOELSCH

KELTIE   SPORK   BOLLINGER   SEELEY

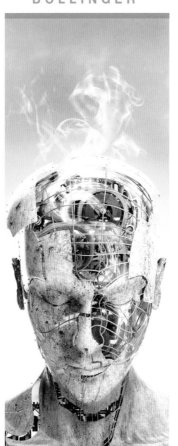

SHANNON ASSOCIATES
212.333.2551

HAAGENSEN

ANDREASEN

HUNT

WARD

SAWYER

KMET

ZAREVA

MORROW

shannonassociates.com

LECOUFFE-DEHARME KOLESOVA NORDSTRAND NIELSEN

COCOZZA REBENSCHIED PETERS HEATH

SHANNON ASSOCIATES
212.333.2551

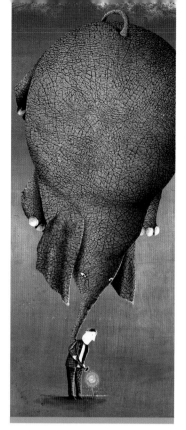

AYESTARAN   BERNASCONI   BONATAKIS   COMPORT

HANS   HENDERLING   KENNEDY   NEUFELD

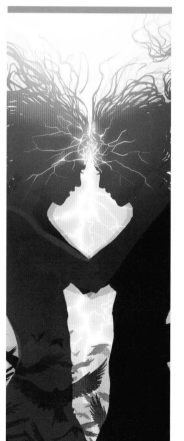

KOEN   KABAN   KINSELLA   TO

PARK   MADRID   CAMPION   BALBUSSO

SHANNON ASSOCIATES
212.333.2551

RAY   CRAIG PHILLIPS   DAVE PHILLIPS   ROE

SWAAB   PRICE   PLATI   O'TOOLE

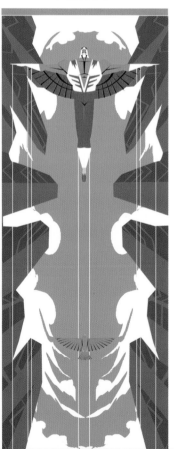

shannonassociates.com

GUERLAIS   RICHARDSON   CAPARO   VIDAL

LOMBARDI   SANTOSO   HOLGATE   KOSTENKO

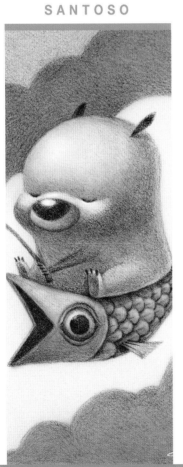

LEONARD

HOLDER

BERNARDIN

BARRETT

TERCIO

LAUGHEAD

HEINZEN

CORTS

shannonassociates.com

  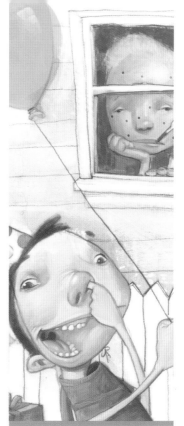 

PICKERING   GILPIN   DIBLEY   LIDDIARD

MOURNING   CALL   COWDREY   MADSEN

SHANNON ASSOCIATES
212.333.2551

BRUNDAGE

CHAU

RIVAS

BENDALL-BRUNELLO

BATES

BELL

DOUGLAS

BLACKMORE

CHRISTY

HALE

CASTELAO

FABBRETTI

HANSEN

BRICKING

HANSON

CALO

SHANNON ASSOCIATES
212.333.2551

KATH

WAKEFIELD

SIMON

LEICK

SAKAMOTO

GOLDEN

FRANCIS

CURTIS

KEELE   MORA   SHROADES   WEBER

JACK   OLSON   PARKS   MCMORRIS

JON REINFURT
+ + + + + + + + + + + + + + + + + +
ILLUSTRATION

GERALD & CULLEN RAPP
212.889.3337
WWW.RAPPART.COM
INFO@RAPPART.COM

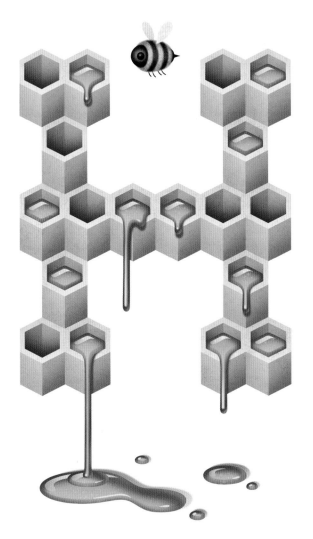

Pushart
Gerald & Cullen Rapp
212 889 3337
info@rappart.com
www.rappart.com

www.pushart.com

Shaw Nielsen
SHAWNIELSEN.COM

GERALD & CULLEN RAPP
WWW.RAPPART.COM
INFO@RAPPART.COM
212-889-3337

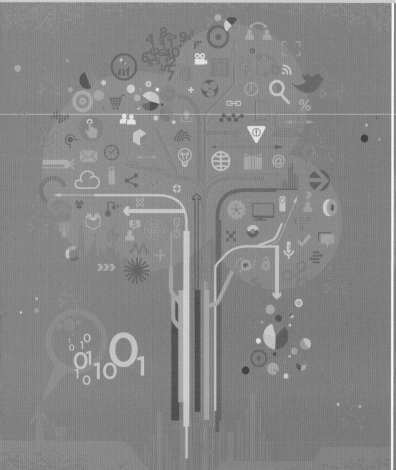

CELIA JOHNSON

GERALD & CULLEN RAPP   info@rappart.com

212 889 3337   www.rappart.com

TRACI DABERKO
GERALD & CULLEN RAPP www.rappart.com
EMAIL: info@rappart.com PHONE: 212.889.3337

CHI BIRMINGHAM

represented by
GERALD & CULLEN RAPP
info@rappart.com
www.rappart.com
(T) 212.889.3337

DANIEL HERTZBERG

Represented by
Gerald & Cullen Rapp
(212) 889-3337
info@rappart.com

www.danielhertzberg.com
www.rappart.com

HANKOSUNA
Gerald & Cullen Rapp

212.889.2227

INFO@RAPPART.COM
WWW.RAPPART.COM
WWW.HANKOSUNA.COM

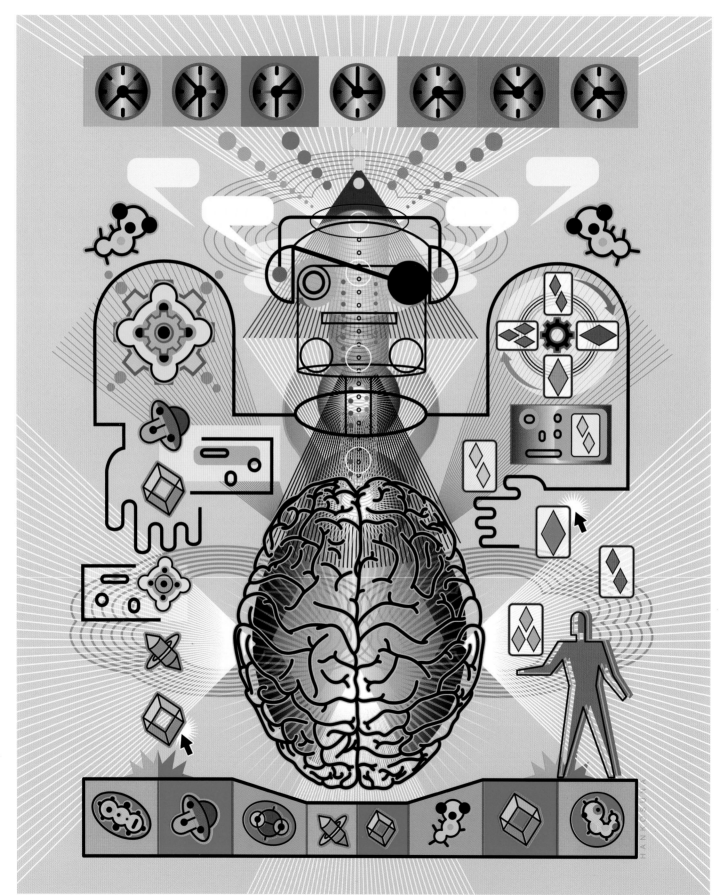

Bruce Morser

Gerald & Cullen Rapp
212 889 3337
info@rappart.com
www.rappart.com

SUMMARY ANNUAL REPORT

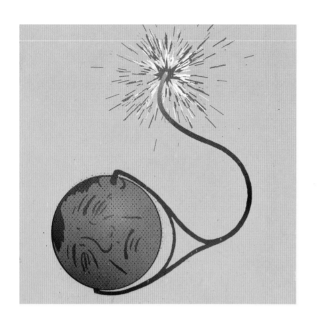

Dan Page

Gerald & Cullen Rapp
212-889-3337
info@rappart.com
www.rappart.com

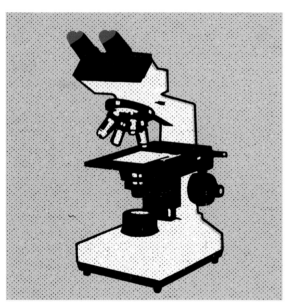

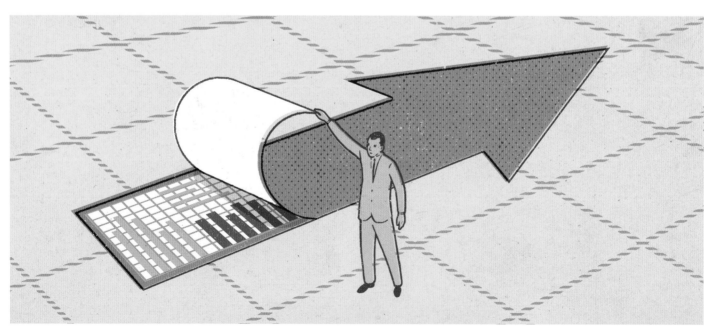

Peter and Maria Hoey
are represented by:
Gerald and Cullen Rapp

212.889.3337
info@rappart.com
peterhoey.com

NEW YORK STOCK EXCHANGE

HOW DOES AN IPO WORK AT THE NYSE?

4 THE PRICE IS SET
THE NIGHT BEFORE THE IPO, THE PRICE OF THE STOCK IS SET BASED ON INVESTOR INTEREST. MONEY IS GIVEN TO THE COMPANY AND IN EXCHANGE FOR INVESTORS RECEIVE SHARES, SOME PORTION OF WHICH WILL BE SOLD ON THE STOCK MARKET THE NEXT MORNING.

5 NYSE BELL RINGING™ CEREMONY

1 THE DECISION
A PRIVATELY-OWNED COMPANY DECIDES TO SEEK OUTSIDE INVESTORS IN ORDER TO RAISE MONEY.

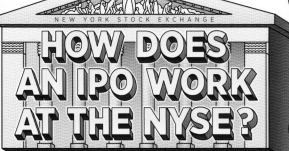

6 WAIT FOR IT...
THE NYSE OPENING BELL® SIGNALS THE START OF TRADING FOR THE U.S. STOCK MARKET, BUT NOT FOR THE SHARES OF AN IPO. BEFORE THE IPO BEGINS TRADING, A PRICE DISCOVERY PROCESS OCCURS, WHICH IS UNIQUE TO THE NYSE.

7 A HUMAN TOUCH
HUMAN INVOLVEMENT AND TRANSPARENCY ARE THE KEY TO THE NYSE PROCESS. THE DESIGNATED MARKET MAKER, OR DMM, LEADS THE PRICE DISCOVERY PROCESS TO FIND THE RIGHT PRICE AT WHICH THE STOCK SHOULD OPEN AND BEGIN TRADING. THIS REQUIRES CLOSE COMMUNICATION WITH KEY CONSTITUENTS IN THE MARKET REGARDING SUPPLY AND DEMAND.

8 PRICE DISCOVERY
THE DMM RUNS AN "AUCTION" FOR THE STOCK. THE AUCTION PROCESS POSITIONS THE DMM IN THE CENTER, WITH BUYERS ON ONE SIDE AND SELLERS ON THE OTHER. THIS PROCESS MAY USE AN OPENING PRICE RANGE — OR A PRICING INDICATION — WHICH IS A DOLLAR RANGE THAT GIVES BUYERS AND SELLERS VISIBILITY INTO INTEREST AND AN OPPORTUNITY TO WEIGH THEIR DESIRE TO PARTICIPATE IN EARLY TRADING.

9 SETTING THE OPENING PRICE
THE INDICATION CAN BE UPDATED SEVERAL TIMES THROUGHOUT THE AUCTION PROCESS AND ULTIMATELY NARROWED TO A SINGLE PRICE, WHICH IS THEN LOCKED IN, AND THE STOCK OPENS FOR TRADING.

2 NOTIFYING THE GOVERNMENT
THE COMPANY MUST SUBMIT A DETAILED DISCLOSURE DOCUMENT EXPLAINING ITS BUSINESS, FINANCIAL RESULTS, STRATEGIES AND RISK FACTORS TO THE SEC.

3 GENERATING INTEREST
THE COMPANY GOES ON AN INVESTOR ROADSHOW WHERE MANAGEMENT SHARES A PRESENTATION ABOUT THE COMPANY WITH INSTITUTIONAL INVESTORS. THE PRESENTATION IS ALSO MADE AVAILABLE FOR RETAIL INVESTORS TO VIEW ONLINE.

BUY SELL

THE BOOK IS FROZEN!

10 THE STOCK IS OPEN FOR TRADING AND A NEW CHAPTER IN A COMPANY'S LIFE BEGINS.
NYSE LISTED

STEPHANIE DALTON COWAN

represented by: gerald & cullen rapp   212.889.3337   www.rappart.com   info@rappart.com   www.daltoncowan.com

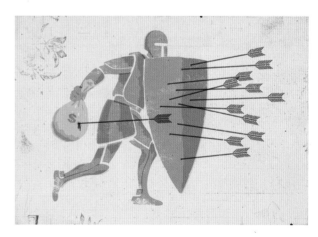

Gerald & Cullen Rapp | 212-889-3337 | info@rappart.com | www.rappart.com

Richard Mia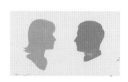

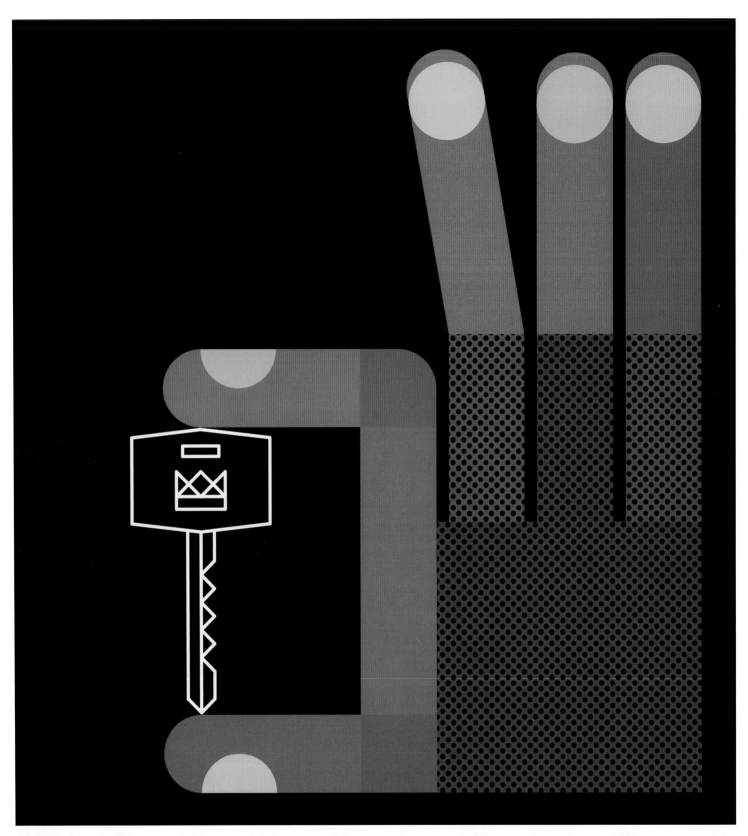

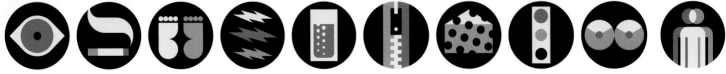

Greg Mably
Gerald & Cullen Rapp • 212.889.3337 • info@rappart.com
gregmably.com • rappart.com

Jean-Manuel Duvivier

represented by Gerald & Cullen Rapp

212-889-3337
info@rappart.com
www.rappart.com

★ NIGEL BUCHANAN Represented by Gerald and Cullen Rapp
212.889.3337 info@rappart.com www.rappart.com www.nigelbuchanan.com

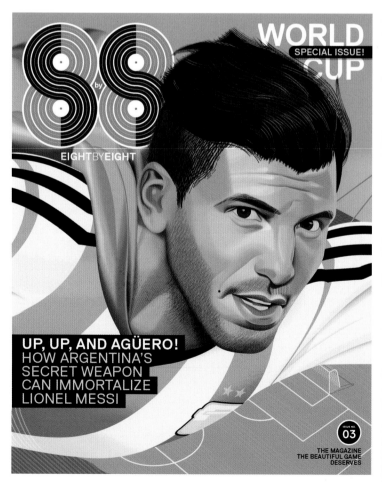

Robert Neubecker
Gerald & Cullen Rapp
212 889 3337
info@rappart.com
www.rappart.com

Michael Witte
Gerald & Cullen Rapp
212 889 3337
info@rappart.com
www.rappart.com

Mark Fredrickson
Gerald & Cullen Rapp
212-889-3337 www.rappart.com
info@rappart.com

BERNARD MAISNER
HAND - LETTERING
REPRESENTED BY
GERALD & CULLEN RAPP
212 - 889 - 3337
WWW.RAPPART.COM
INFO@RAPPART.COM

Absolutely Loise

CHATEAU BOSWELL
PINOT NOIR
Sonoma Coast, Sonoma County
2012

The Surf Issue

LIVING WELL in STL

Charles Scott • Brian Toms • Melissa LeBran • Lawrence McSlone • Scott Burdelik • Ronald Bourg • Daniel Jumps • Steve Xulas • Peter Owen • Mark David Finke • Barry Alves • Caldwell Robert Hendrix • Dave Hart • Andrew Elrod • Daniel Littell • Rick Patel • Mario Seman • Shannon Miller • Eric Storz • John Bodnar • Joseph Malley • Robert Krepps • Joe Ferriero • Lettie Frease • Frank Scripa • Peter Hern • Paul Reeves • Janice Allen • Thomas Deery • Shawn Habba • Hai Nguyen • James Balder • Lorenzo Bodie • Russell Kramer • Mac Hughes • Anthony Garbo • Jovon Roe • David Fraire • Joseph Collins • J. Edwards, Jr. • Paul Siangrande • Todd Vetsch • Daniel Taylor • David Buhler • Joshua Edmondson • VanCarlo Garcia • James Montroy • Martin Gonzalez • Walter Jacbsen • Lance Bobby Thigpen • Mark Woelppel • Richard Garrie • Scott Batchelder • Jeffrey Gayari • Caudill Anthony Paladino • Miriam Iglesias • James Waldrop • Mark Lawretta • Michael Carmody • Thomas Powers • Scott Oliverio • Anthony Griffith • Jerry Burnard • Nicholas Wilson • Matthew Garchow • Ed Rodriguez • Chevist Mitchell • Nanette Vizachero • Khalil Benazouz • Robert Emmrich • Richard Garbo • Gary Baehmann • Travis Gluknecht • Alex Soyfer • Paul Solari • T. Shane Donaldson • Roger Tatsch, Jr. • Marty Rutkowski • John • Scott Wayne @Labretta • Michaels • Grinstead • Nasser Alibakhsh • Henry • John Hrynyszyn @ Bridgeman • Peter Radlowski @ AN • Wael Mouzahem, Esq. • Scott Lefever, Esq.

LINDGREN ▪ SMITH
{212} 397-7330

Jerome Studer

LINDGRENSMITH.COM
INFO@LSILLUSTRATION.COM

D A V I D
G O L D M A N
A G E N C Y

Since 1980 proudly
representing the nicest and
most intelligent people, who just
happen to be extraordinary
Illustrators & Designers.

p: 212-807-6627 • **www.davidgoldmanagency.com** • dg@davidgoldmanagency.com • @DGANYC

Bendell

normbendell.com

Proudly Represented by:

David Goldman Agency

www.davidgoldmanagency.com 212-807-6627 *dg@davidgoldmanagency.com*

"The Impolite Gentleman" impolitegentleman.tumblr.com

Computerworld, April Montgomery-AD   World Bank, Mihae Kim-GD   Dallas Morning News, Mike Hogue-AD

Teatro Alla Scala, Tita Milano, Helene LeCannu-GD

James Yang is proudly represented by DAVID GOLDMAN AGENCY
p: 212-807-6627 • **www.davidgoldmanagency.com** • dg@davidgoldmanagency.com • @DGANYC

www.stevedininno.com

Steve Dininno is proudly represented by DAVID GOLDMAN AGENCY
p: 212-807-6627 • www.davidgoldmanagency.com • dg@davidgoldmanagency.com • @DGANYC

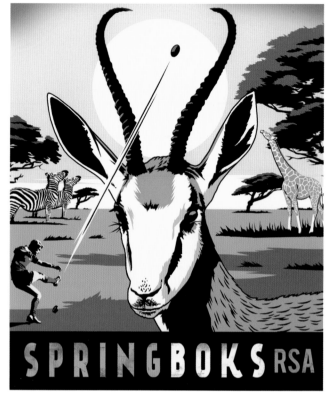

Bill Butcher is proudly represented by DAVID GOLDMAN AGENCY
p: 212-807-6627 • www.davidgoldmanagency.com • dg@davidgoldmanagency.com • @DGANYC

brunomallart.com

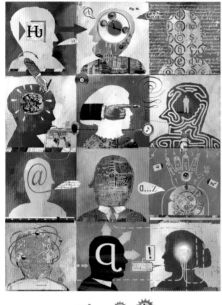

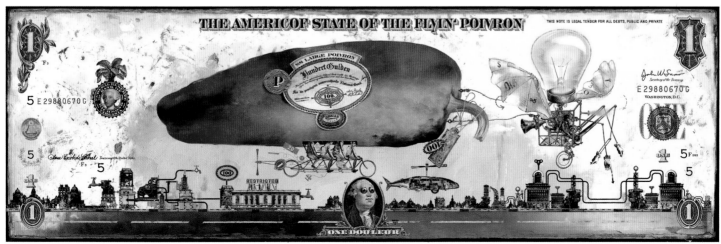

Bruno Mallart is proudly represented by DAVID GOLDMAN AGENCY
p: 212-807-6627 • **www.davidgoldmanagency.com** • dg@davidgoldmanagency.com • @DGANYC

DAVIDFOSTERGRAPHICS.COM

SOUTHFIELD   8 MILE   OAK PARK   FERNDALE   WARREN

GRAND RIVER

HIGHLAND
PARK

HAMTRAMCK

FORD

DEARBORN

WIN

MICHIGAN
INKSTER   DEARBORN
HEIGHTS

RIVER ROUGE

FRAMEWORK ZONE
- GREATER DOWNT
- LOW VACANCY
- MODERATE VACA
- HIGH VACANCY

SOURCE: DWPLTP TECHN

AILES   1   2   4

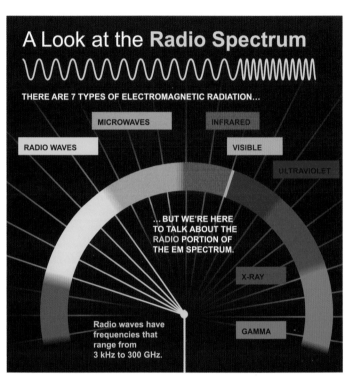

A Look at the **Radio Spectrum**

THERE ARE 7 TYPES OF ELECTROMAGNETIC RADIATION...

MICROWAVES   INFRARED

RADIO WAVES   VISIBLE

ULTRAVIOLET

...BUT WE'RE HERE
TO TALK ABOUT THE
RADIO PORTION OF
THE EM SPECTRUM.

X-RAY

GAMMA

Radio waves have
frequencies that
range from
3 kHz to 300 GHz.

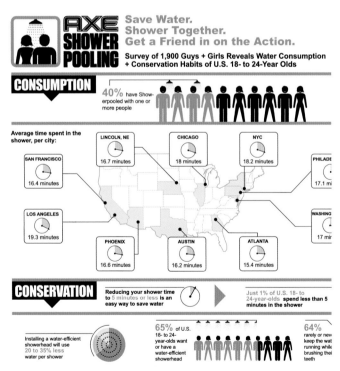

AXE SHOWER POOLING

Save Water.
Shower Together.
Get a Friend in on the Action.

Survey of 1,900 Guys + Girls Reveals Water Consumption
+ Conservation Habits of U.S. 18- to 24-Year Olds

CONSUMPTION

40% have Show-
erpooled with one or
more people

Average time spent in the
shower, per city:

LINCOLN, NE — 16.7 minutes
CHICAGO — 18 minutes
NYC — 18.2 minutes
SAN FRANCISCO — 16.4 minutes
PHILADE — 17.1 mi
LOS ANGELES — 19.3 minutes
WASHING — 17 min
PHOENIX — 16.6 minutes
AUSTIN — 16.2 minutes
ATLANTA — 15.4 minutes

CONSERVATION

Reducing your shower time
to 5 minutes or less **is an
easy way to save water**

Just 1% of U.S. 18- to
24-year-olds spend less than 5
minutes in the shower

Installing a water-efficient
showerhead will use
20 to 35% less
water per shower

65% of U.S.
18- to 24-
year-olds want
or have a
water-efficient
showerhead

64%
rarely or nev
keep the wat
running while
brushing thei
teeth

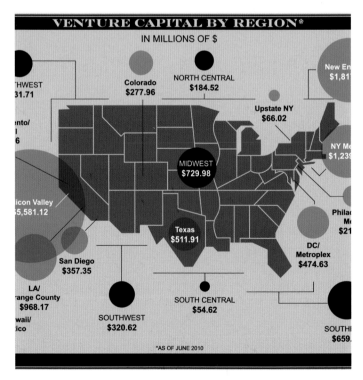

VENTURE CAPITAL BY REGION*

IN MILLIONS OF $

NHWEST
31.71

Colorado
$277.96

NORTH CENTRAL
$184.52

New En
$1,81

Upstate NY
$66.02

ento/
6

NY Me
$1,239

MIDWEST
$729.98

icon Valley
5,581.12

Texas
$511.91

Philad
Me
$21

San Diego
$357.35

DC/
Metroplex
$474.63

LA/
range County
$968.17

SOUTH CENTRAL
$54.62

waii/
ico

SOUTHWEST
$320.62

SOUTHI
$659.

*AS OF JUNE 2010

DAVID FOSTER is proudly represented by DAVID GOLDMAN AGENCY
p: 212-807-6627 • **www.davidgoldmanagency.com** • dg@davidgoldmanagency.com

JIMDRYDEN.COM

the donor advised fund
The Minneapolis Foundation | Freedom to Focus on Your Giving

Jim Dryden is proudly represented by DAVID GOLDMAN AGENCY
p: 212-807-6627 • www.davidgoldmanagency.com • dg@davidgoldmanagency.com • @DGANYC

RAGiNG PiG

BAR & GRILL

Jack-in-a-Box
PRODUCTIONS

lina **carrillo**
represented by
Lemonade illustration agency
www.lemonadeillustration.com
+44 (0)7891 390750

UNIVERSITY
Engaging the culture,
changing the world.

3307 Third Avenue West, Suite 116
Seattle, Washington 98119-1922
spu.edu
beckyo@spu.edu

helen **huang**
represented by
Lemonade illustration agency
www.lemonadeillustration.com
+44 (0)7891 390750

paul **dickinson**

represented by

Lemonade illustration agency

www.lemonadeillustration.com

+44 (0)7891 390750

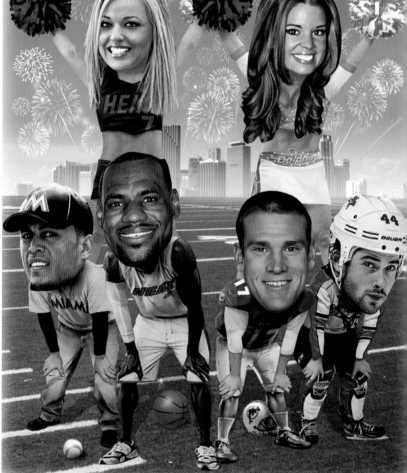

chris **dickason**
represented by Lemonade illustration agency
www.lemonadeillustration.com +44 (0)7891 390750

nozomi **inoue**
represented by **Lemonade** illustration agency
www.lemonadeillustration.com +44 (0)7891 390750

Dating the Animal Way

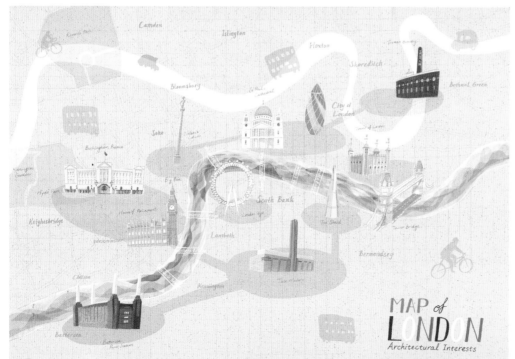

MAP of LONDON
Architectural Interests

Blueberry Flapjack

Cal her

Muffins

Nata

granola with berries

eran **mendel**
represented by Lemonade illustration agency
www.lemonadeillustration.com +44 (0)7891 390750

www.folioart.co.uk / +44 (0)20 7242 9562 / info@folioart.co.uk

Click here

THE MAGAZINE FOR RESEARCH AND BUSINESS COLLABORATORS

REALISE

RESEARCH + COLLABORATION + INNOVATION

LIFE CHANGING
World Shaping

w: www.folioart.co.uk
e: info@folioart.co.uk
t: +44 (0)20 7242 9562

Owen Davey

183

FALL IN LOVE WITH THE
PORTUGAL MASTERS

184

w: www.folioart.co.uk
e: info@folioart.co.uk
t: +44 (0)20 7242 9562

Rui Ricardo

w: www.folioart.co.uk
e: info@folioart.co.uk
t: +44 (0)20 7242 9562

Karolis Strautniekas

w: www.folioart.co.uk
e: info@folioart.co.uk
t: +44 (0)20 7242 9562

Nabil Nezzar

w: www.folioart.co.uk
e: info@folioart.co.uk
t: +44 (0)20 7242 9562

Carolyn Jenkins

w: www.folioart.co.uk
e: info@folioart.co.uk
t: +44 (0)20 7242 9562

Nicholas Stevenson

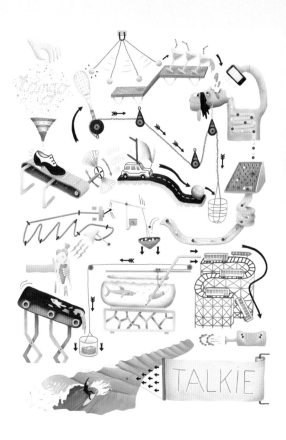

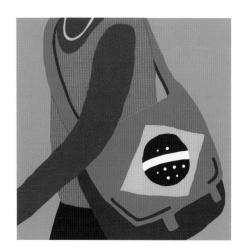

w: www.folioart.co.uk
e: info@folioart.co.uk
t: +44 (0)20 7242 9562

Antoine Corbineau

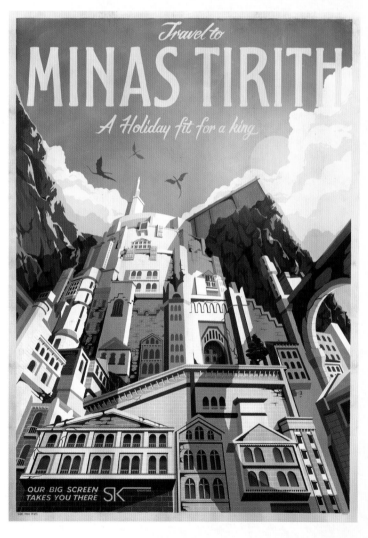

w: www.folioart.co.uk
e: info@folioart.co.uk
t: +44 (0)20 7242 9562

190

Studio Muti

XVII

EL DOMADOR

XXXII

EL CALVO

w: www.folioart.co.uk
e: info@folioart.co.uk
t: +44 (0)20 7242 9562

Julian De Narvaez

191

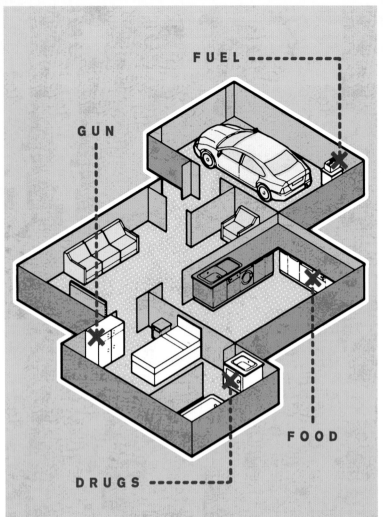

FUEL

GUN

FOOD

DRUGS

RAIN

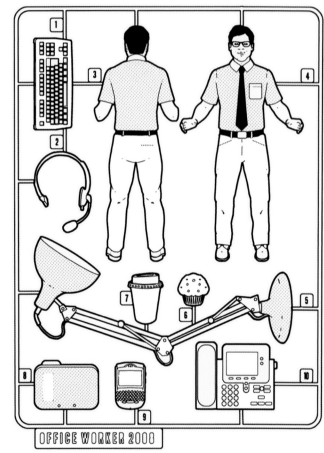

OFFICE WORKER 2008

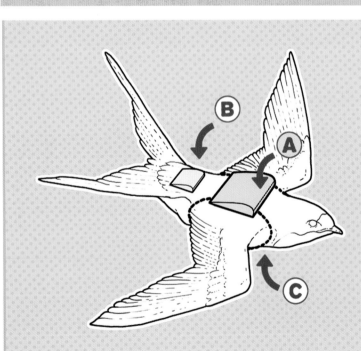

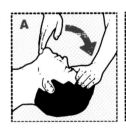

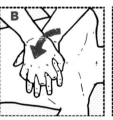

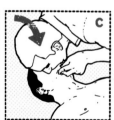

w: www.folioart.co.uk
e: info@folioart.co.uk
t: +44 (0)20 7242 9562

Son Of Alan

w: www.folioart.co.uk
e: info@folioart.co.uk
t: +44 (0)20 7242 9562

Jessica Dance

193

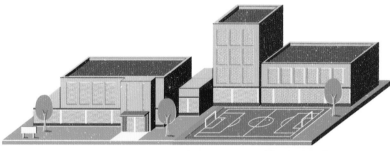

w: www.folioart.co.uk
e: info@folioart.co.uk
t: +44 (0)20 7242 9562

194

Toby Leigh

w: www.folioart.co.uk
e: info@folioart.co.uk
t: +44 (0)20 7242 9562

Britta Stenhouse

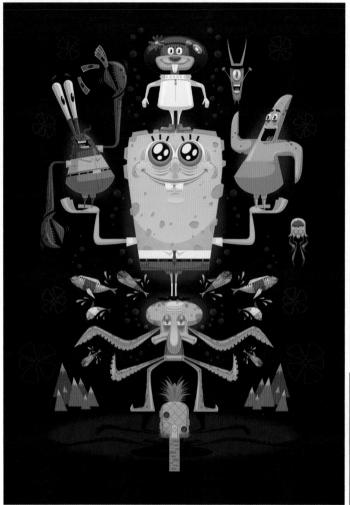

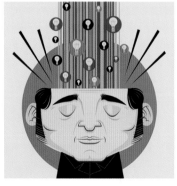

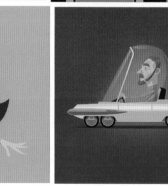

w: www.folioart.co.uk
e: info@folioart.co.uk
t: +44 (0)20 7242 9562

James Gilleard

Ricardo Bessa

 w: www.folioart.co.uk
e: info@folioart.co.uk
t: +44 (0)20 7242 9562

Alex Green

Bruce Emmett

w: www.folioart.co.uk
e: info@folioart.co.uk
t: +44 (0)20 7242 9562

Roger Watt

Finn Campbell Notman

w: www.folioart.co.uk
e: info@folioart.co.uk
t: +44 (0)20 7242 9562

Lisa Evans

Peter Tarka

w: www.folioart.co.uk
e: info@folioart.co.uk
t: +44 (0)20 7242 9562

Mega Pont

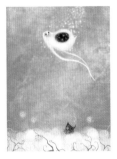

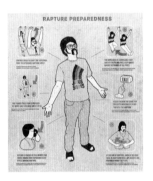

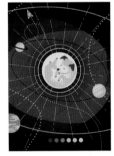

w: www.folioart.co.uk
e: info@folioart.co.uk
t: +44 (0)20 7242 9562

Folio Shop

Orlando Arocena

Patrick Arrasmith

Niklas Asker

Kent Barton

James Bennett

Maria Corte Maidagan

Paul Cox

Kinuko Y Craft

Eric Drooker

110 E 30th Street
Suite 501
New York, NY 10016

212 223 9545 · 917 841 1333
richard@richardsolomon.com
www.richardsolomon.com

ichał Dziekan

Thomas Ehretsmann

Jon Foster

hris Gall

Rudy Gutierrez

Tyler Jacobson

avid Johnson

Gary Kelley

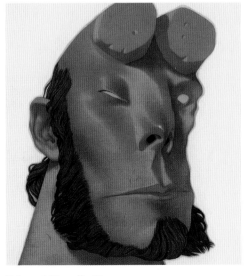

Edward Kinsella III

Dongyun Lee

Gregory Manchess

Ricardo Martínez

John Mattos

Goñi Montes

Tran Nguyen

Karla Ortiz

David Palumbo

CF Payne

- 110 E 30th Street
Suite 501
New York, NY 10016

- 212 223 9545 · 917 841 1333
richard@richardsolomon.com
www.richardsolomon.com

l Sanderson

Jason Seiler

Douglas Smith

ark T Smith

Sam Spratt

Guy Stauber

hase Stone

Mark Summers

Ted Wright

MENDOLA

portfolio
mendolaart.com

email
info@mendolaart.com

call
212.986.5680

represents
THE 3D AGENCY

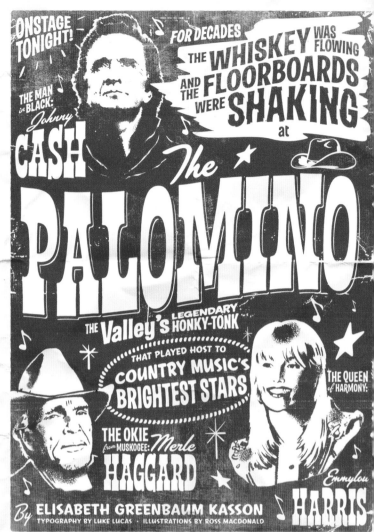

MENDOLA

portfolio
mendolaart.com

email
info@mendolaart.com

call
212.986.5680

represents
LUKE LUCAS

MENDOLA

portfolio
mendolaart.com

email
info@mendolaart.com

call
212.986.5680

represents
DAHL TAYLOR

209

MENDOLA

portfolio
mendolaart.com

email
info@mendolaart.com

call
212.986.5680

represents
AMY DEVOOGD

DEATH IS SO FINAL
WHEREAS LIFE IS FULL OF POSSIBILITIES

YOU HEAR THEM, BOY?
THE OLD GODS ARE ANSWERING YOU

MENDOLA

portfolio
mendolaart.com

email
info@mendolaart.com

call
212.986.5680

represents
ROBERT BALL

211

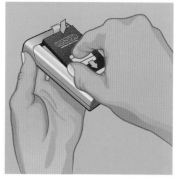

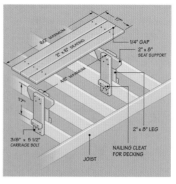

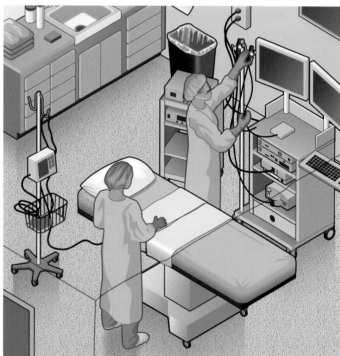

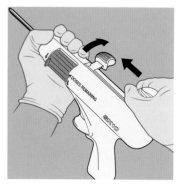

MENDOLA

portfolio
mendolaart.com

email
info@mendolaart.com

call
212.986.5680

represents
KOPP ILLUSTRATION

MENDOLA portfolio
mendolaart.com

email
info@mendolaart.com

call
212.986.5680

represents
HUGH SYME

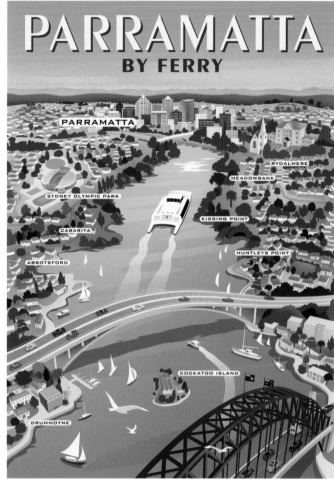

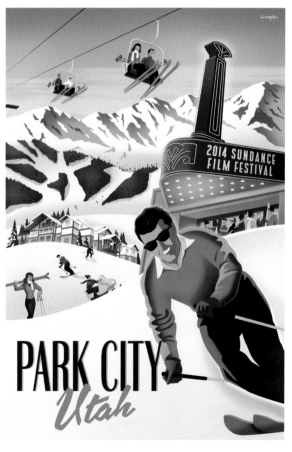

MENDOLA

portfolio
mendolaart.com

email
info@mendolaart.com

call
212.986.5680

represents
MICHAEL CRAMPTON

214

MENDOLA

portfolio
mendolaart.com

email
info@mendolaart.com

call
212.986.5680

represents
THE IMAGE FOUNDATION

EXPLORER'S
REEF
AT SEAWORLD.

MENDOLA
portfolio
mendolaart.com
email
info@mendolaart.com
call
212.986.5680

represents
JEFF MANGIAT

james
SHEPHERD
www.jamesshepherd.com

MENDOLA
ARTISTS REPRESENTATIVES

WWW.MENDOLAART.COM
PH 212.986.5680   E info@mendolaart.com

James Shepherd

2D and 3D
character design
illustration
and animation

MENDOLA

portfolio
mendolaart.com

email
info@mendolaart.com

call
212.986.5680

represents
BILL LEDGER

MENDOLA

220

portfolio
mendolaart.com

email
info@mendolaart.com

call
212.986.5680

represents
RUSSELL BENFANTI
www.benfanti.com

MENDOLA   portfolio
mendolaart.com   email
info@mendolaart.com   call
212.986.5680   represents
KIM & JAMES

MENDOLA

portfolio
mendolaart.com

email
info@mendolaart.com

call
212.986.5680

represents
DAN SIPPLE

MENDOLA

portfolio
mendolaart.com

email
info@menolaart.com

call
212.986.5680

represents
ZUTTO

MENDOLA   portfolio
mendolaart.com   email
info@mendolaart.com   call
212.986.5680   represents
JULIA GREEN

A Architecture

B Broken

C Chester Cheetah

D DaVinci Style

E Engine

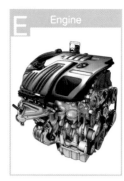
F Farmers Daughter

G Guitar Hero

H Haircare

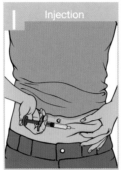
I Injection

J Juice

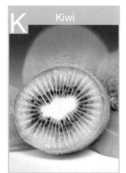
K Kiwi

L Lumberjack

M Mini Cooper

Find Your Solution
www.aareps.com

ph. 212.682.2462

AA
Digital Production Services

AA REPS
Creative for Interactive, Motion & Print

info@aareps.com

N Newlyweds

O Oklahoma

P Portraits

Q Q-Omega Hair

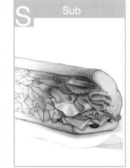
R Racecars

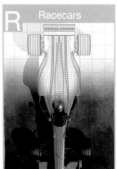
S Sub

T Tea

U Umbrella

V Volcano

W Winegums

X X-Ray

Y Yellow Leathers

Z Zebra

Bill Garland

AA REPS
Since 1920
Creative for interactive, motion & print

Find Your Solution
www.aareps.com

ph.212.682.2462
info@aareps.com

Jerry LoFaro

Find Your Solution
www.aareps.com

AA
Since 1920
AA REPS
reative for interactive, motion & print

ph.212.682.2462
info@aareps.com

www.JOHNHOMSTUDIO.com

John Hom
ILLUSTRATION STUDIO

AA REPS
Since 1920
Creative for interactive, motion & print

Find Your Solution
www.aareps.com

ph.212.682.2462
info@aareps.com

www.JOHNHOMSTUDIO.com

John Hom
ILLUSTRATION STUDIO

AA REPS
Creative for interactive, motion & print
Since 1920

Find Your Solution
www.aareps.com

ph.212.682.2462
info@aareps.com

Marcel Laverdet

AA REPS
Since 1920
Creative for interactive, motion & print

Find Your Solution
www.aareps.com

ph.212.682.2462
info@aareps.com

David Semple

AA REPS
Since 1920
Creative for interactive, motion & print

Find Your Solution
www.aareps.com

ph.212.682.2462
info@aareps.com

Andrew Painter

Since 1920

AA REPS
Creative for interactive, motion & print

Find Your Solution
www.aareps.com

ph.212.682.2462
info@aareps.com

Randy Glass

www.RandyGlassStudio.com

AA REPS
Since 1920
Creative for interactive, motion & print

Find Your Solution
www.aareps.com

ph.212.682.2462
info@aareps.com

Kent Gamble

AA REPS
Since 1920
Creative for interactive, motion & print

Find Your Solution
www.aareps.com

ph.212.682.2462
info@aareps.com

The Sweet Science

$$\frac{\sqrt{5}+1}{2} = 1.618$$

The perfect salty-sweet snack.

AA REPS
Since 1920
Creative for interactive, motion & print

Find Your Solution
www.aareps.com

ph.212.682.2462
info@aareps.com

Giovannina Colalillo

Jim Steck

Geo Parkin

Tony Randazzo

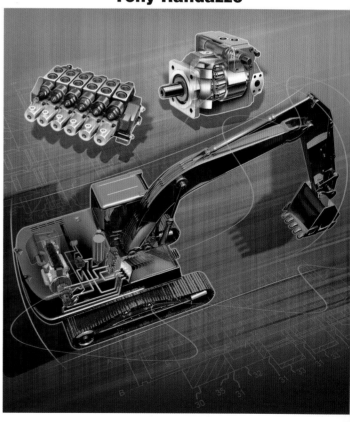

AA
Since 1920

AA REPS
Creative for interactive, motion & print

Find Your Solution
www.aareps.com

ph.212.682.2462
info@aareps.com

Rick Grayson

Mike Bryan

Mike Jaroszko

Matt Zang

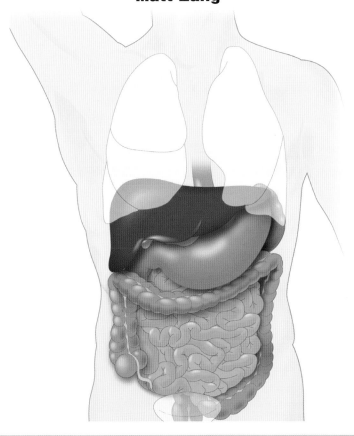

AA
Since 1920
AA REPS
reative for interactive, motion & print

Find Your Solution
www.aareps.com

ph.212.682.2462
info@aareps.com

Glenn Gustafson

Represented by: John Brewster ▪ john@brewstercreative.com ▪ 203.226.4724

Glenn Gustafson

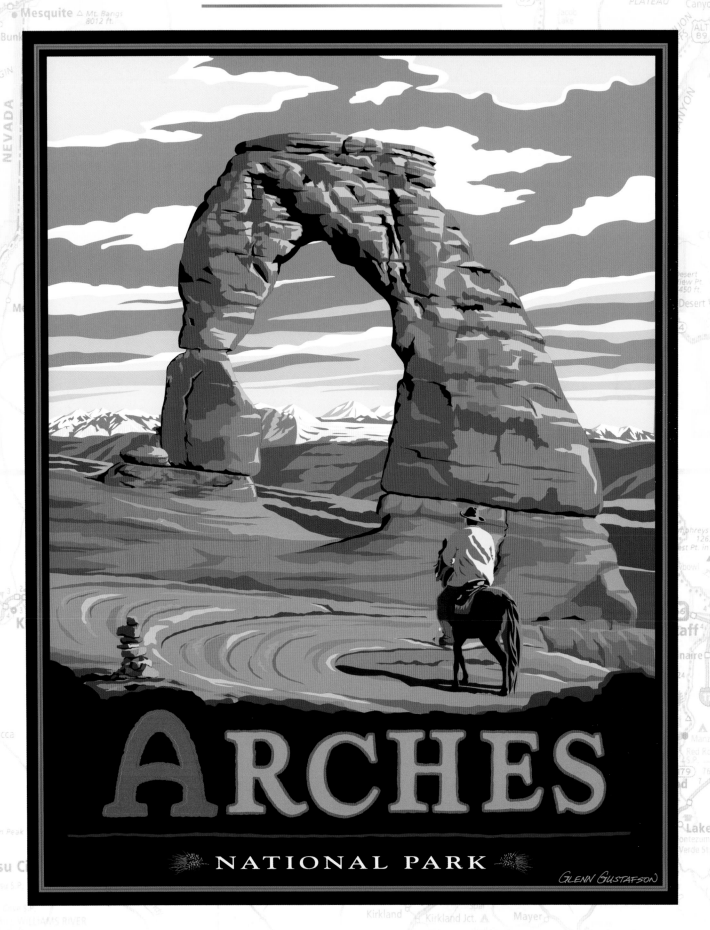

 www.glenngustafson.com • ggustafson2@yahoo.com • Studio 630.947.2785

STEPHEN HARRINGTON
255 WILTON ROAD WEST, RIDGEFIELD, CT 06877
(203)431-5854   E-Mail: sharringtonillus@earthlink.net

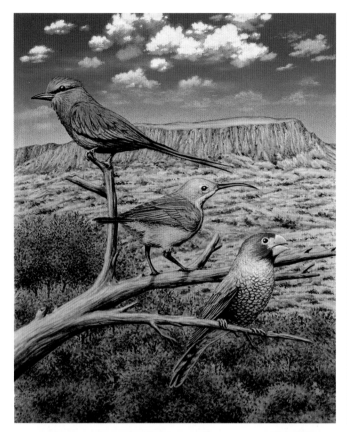

PHONE: (203)226-4724   FAX (203)454-9904
creative svcs.snet.net   www.brewstercreative.com
JOHN BREWSTER CREATIVE SERVICES

JONATHAN & GEORGINA ROSENBAUM

WWW.ROSENBAUMILLUSTRATION.COM
JOHN BREWSTER CREATIVE SERVICES   203·226·4724
JOHN@BREWSTERCREATIVE.COM   WWW.BREWSTERCREATIVE.COM

Susan Tolonen

Michael Backus

Matt Zumbo

Howard McWilliam

blascocreative.com   312.782.0244

Leland Klanderman

ORGANIC FARMING
MAINTAINING SUSTAINABILITY
OF THE **FARMING SYSTEM**

HOMECOMING // BY THE NUMBERS

George Cathey

BLASCO CREATIVE ARTISTS

Douglas Klauba

Matt LeBarre

Marina Seaone

Stephen Brown

Gustavo Ortega

Larry Martin

Heather Holbrook

 BLASCO CREATIVE ARTISTS   blascocreative.com   312.782.0244

Drew Rose

Francesca D'Ottavi

Sarolta Szulyovszky

Wilkinson
STUDIOS, INC
International Agents for Illustration

www.wilkinsonstudios.com
630.549.0504

Estudio Haus
Ilustrators

Jok
Gervasio
Carlos Aon

www.estudiohaus.com.ar

Wilkinson
STUDIOS, INC

www.wilkinsonstudios.com
630-549-0504

Beautifully Quirky
Illustration

Timothy Banks

TIMOTHYBANKS.COM

call 843-297-5800 follow @teabanks
email mail@timothybanks.com

represented by Wilkinson
STUDIOS, INC

call 630-549-0504 visit wilkinsonstudios.com

Global Arts Muse Inc. International Building
45 Rockefeller Plaza at 630 Fifth Avenue
Suite 2000 New York, NY 10111
212.332.5010 fax 212.332.3401
sayitwithart@icloud.com

Challenges Are To Be Met

WindHorse Illustrators

Jef Thompson

I begin with the simplest of sketches knowing that the accidents caused from working with the board will define the illustration much more so than any detailed drawing. The sketch merely suggests the concept and composition whereas the scraping knife will define the finished piece. © 2014 - Mouse & Cat

Global Arts Muse Inc. International Building
45 Rockefeller Plaza at 630 Fifth Avenue
Suite 2000 New York, NY 10111
212.332.5010 fax 212.332.3401
sayitwithart@icloud.com

Challenges Are To Be Met

WindHorse Illustrators

Jef Thompson

I had my first major publication with the National Geographic Society in 1999 and since that time I have worked for such clients as Harper Collins, Houghton Mifflin, Yale University Press, Harcourt, McGraw Hill, Capstone Press, Zondervan, Picture Window Books and Troubadour Games. © 2014 - Lion Tamer

STEVEN TABBUTT

JOSÉE BISAILLON

SIMONA MULAZZANI

MORGANGAYNIN.COM
MORGAN GAYNIN INC.
INFO@MORGANGAYNIN.COM (212)475-0440

SYLVIE DAIGNEAULT

ANSON LIAW

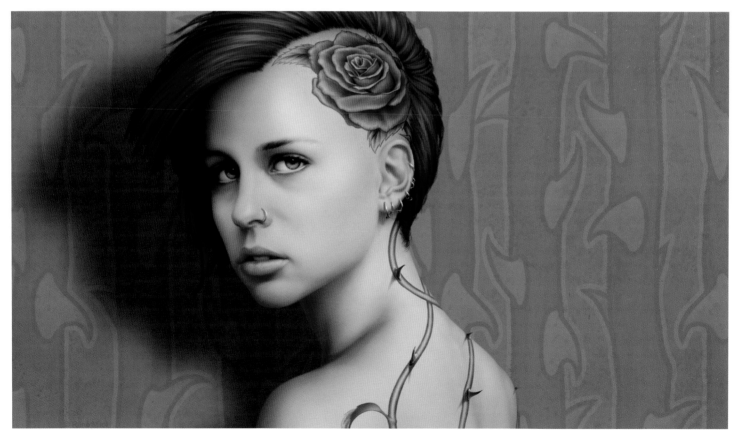

RENÉ MILOT

SALLY VITSKY

PAUL GARLAND

JOYCE PATTI

MORGANGAYNIN.COM
INFO@MORGANGAYNIN.COM (212)475-0440
MORGAN GAYNIN INC.

A. RICHARD ALLEN

SUSAN GAL

LAURA TALLARDY

MORGANGAYNIN.COM
INFO@MORGANGAYNIN.COM
MORGAN GAYNIN INC.
(212) 475-0440

Doug Sirois

Andrew Farley

Cristina Guitian

Edmond Davis

Nick Chaffe

Patrick Knowles

Meiklejohn

Inspiring Illustration

Hannah George

Garry Walton

Gary Redford

Ben Scruton

Garry Parsons

Paul Boston

+44 (0)207 593 0500
info@meiklejohn.co.uk
www.meiklejohn.co.uk
259

Barbara Spoettel

Gavin Reece

Emma Brownjohn

Nila Aye

Sean Sims

Barbara Von Tannenberg

New Division

Inspiring Illustration

Carrie May

Lucy Truman

Rich Wake

Gary Newman

Ana Seixas

Robyn Neild

+44 (0)207 593 0505
info@newdivision.com
www.newdivision.com

Rich Wake

Hannah George

Carrie May

Doug Sirois

Nila Aye

Paul Boston

Meiklejohn   New Division   Kids Corner

Inspiring Illustration

Andrew Farley

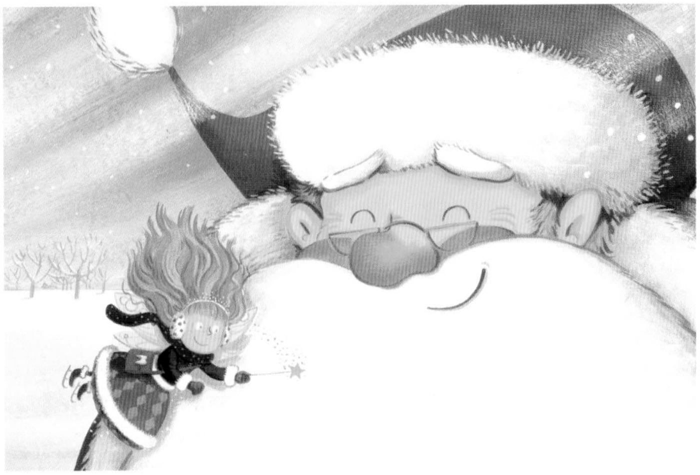

Garry Parsons

Anna Hymas

Ben Scruton

Sean Sims

Lucy Truman

+44 (0)207 593 0500

info@meiklejohn.co.uk

www.meiklejohn.co.uk/kidscorner

MB artists

MELA BOLINAO T 212 689.7830 F 212 689.7829 www.mbartists.com

CAROLINA FARíAS

CLAUDINE GÉVRY

TAMMIE LYON

RÉMY SIMARD

mb MB artists

Serge Seidlitz

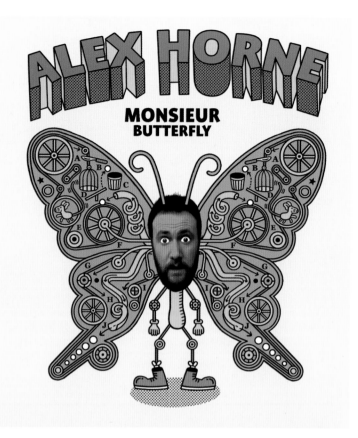

Represented By

BERNSTEIN & ANDRIULLI

www.ba-reps.com | *58 West 40th Street New York NY 10018* | *212.682.1490*

MARK COLLINS

BOB KAYGANICH

DAN MCGEEHAN

ROBIN BOYER

NANCY HARRISON

SCOTT BURROUGHS

NANCY HARRISON

SHARON AND JOEL HARRIS

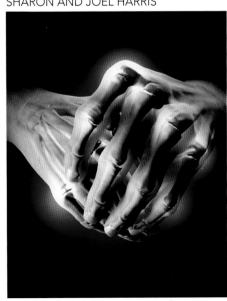

JESSE REISCH

NICOLE ALESI

DAVID MOORE

IAN SEO

NATHALIE BEAUVOIS

PETER RICHARDSON

DEDE PUTRA

BILL BRUNING

RALPH VOLTZ

JERRY HOARE

215.232.6666   illustrationOnLine.com   DEBORAH WOLFE LTD

ROSS JONES

AMY WUMMER

DARON PARTON

GERAD TAYLOR

GREG COPELAND

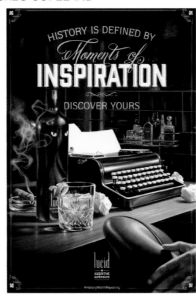

LAURA WATSON

ERIC YOUNG

JOHN SCHREINER

SIMON SHAW

Illustration & Moving Image
Creative Visual Consultancy

AgencyRush*

+44 (0) 1273 675 122
info@agencyrush.com
www.agencyrush.com

Specsavers

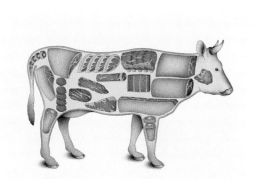

Illustration & Moving Image
Creative Visual Consultancy

AgencyRush*

+44 (0) 1273 675 122
info@agencyrush.com
www.agencyrush.com

LILLA ROGERS STUDIO

PHONE NO. **781.641.2787**

WEB **WWW.LILLAROGERS.COM**

Representing artists internationally

LILLA
ROGERS
STUDIO

LISA DEJOHN

JILLIAN PHILLIPS

ZOE INGRAM

ALLISON COLE

SUZY ULTMAN

SARAJO FRIEDEN

SILVIA DEKKER

LISA CONGDON

CAROLYN GAVIN

Good Morning

MARCO MARELLA

DANIEL ROODE

MACRINA BUSATO

THANK YOU

TRINA DALZIEL

Happy Birthday Lilla!

AMY BLAY

WISHING YOU... GOOD TiMES WiTH FRIENDS, COOL TUNES FUN and LAUGHTER...

HELEN DARDIK

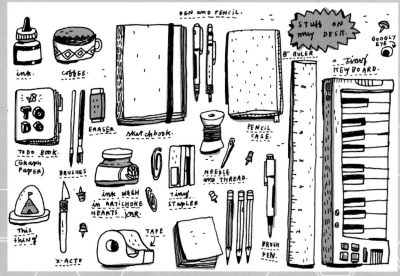

MIKE LOWERY

THE ILLUSTRATION ROOM

Paolo Lim

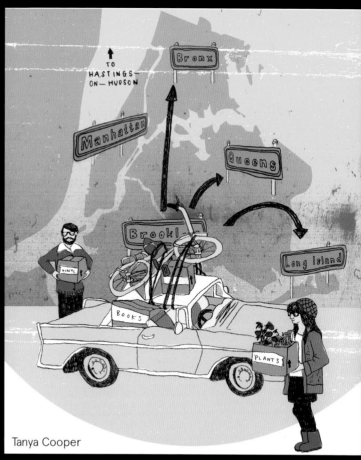

Tanya Cooper

Gregory Baldwin

Andrea Smith

Angie Réhe

Elisa Mazzone

Maude Guesne

Igor Morski

The Project Twins

Chris Edser

THE ILLUSTRATION ROOM

Steven Van Hasten

your
Charm
fragrance

Jacqueline Bissett

Illustration

Contact Stacey or Karen at:
E howdy@illustrationweb.com
T 646.808.0205
W illustrationweb.com

70A Greenwich Ave #278
New York
NY 10011

#WEAREILLUSTRATION

Representing over 100 of the World's Most Talented Illustrators

MELISSA **IWAI**

LISA **FIELDS**

CHRISTINA **TUGEAU**
chris@catugeau.com

CATUGEAU : ARTIST AGENCY

www.catugeau.com

CHRISTY **EWERS**
christy@catugeau.com

757 221 0666

MERYL **TREATNER**

ANA **OCHOA**

KELLY **KENNEDY**

NINA **MATA**

CHRISTINA **TUGEAU**
chris@catugeau.com

www.catugeau.com

CATUGEAU : ARTIST AGENCY
CATUGEAU : ARTIST AGENCY

CHRISTY **EWERS**
christy@catugeau.com

757 221 0666

CATHY **GENDRON**

LAURA **LOGAN**

JOEL SPECTOR

JOSE RAMOS

Easter Express

DAN SHARP

The Neis Group

NEISGROUP.COM   616.450.1533

ROBERT SAUBER

JOHN WHITE

The
Neis
Group

NEISGROUP.COM
616.450.1533

Linda de Moreta
R E P R E S E N T S

James Yamasaki Illustration

Please visit www.lindareps.com, or call us at 510.769.1421
Or email linda@lindareps.com. We'd love to hear from you!

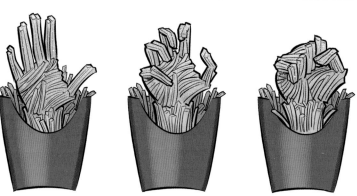

Peter McDonnell Illustration

Please visit www.lindareps.com, or call us at 510.769.1421
Or email linda@lindareps.com. We'd love to hear from you!

Linda
de Moreta
R E P R E S E N T S

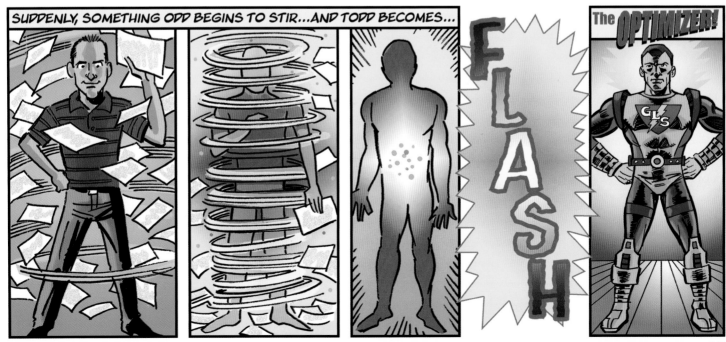

scott snow

randy royter

tim washburn

tim washburn

RHYNEREPRESENTS.COM

PAULETTE R RHYNE

artist representative

No.303.871.9166

CHARMED VooDoo
HIBISCUS TISANE

allan burch

allan burch

carly schonberg

john huxtable

RHYNEREPRESENTS.COM

PAULETTE RHYNE

artist representative

No.303.871.9166

Christer Eriksson

Christer Eriksson

Bruce Hutchison

artagent.com

Kym Foster

Carol Guenzi Agents /ArtAgent.com   800.417.5120   art@artagent.com   www.artagent.com

Copyright © 2014 by Michelle Barbera

Michelle Barbera
tel: 781.572.5352

www.barberaillustration.com
michelle@barberaillustration.com

Copyright © 2014 by Michelle Barbera

Michelle Barbera
tel: 781.572.5352

www.barberaillustration.com
michelle@barberaillustration.com

BRAND NU

art direction, illustration and typography

[London . UK]

hello@brandnu.co.uk
+44 7881 646 808

see full folio at
www.brandnu.co.uk

STEVEN NOBLE

| SCRATCHBOARD | LINE ART | ENGRAVINGS | WOODCUTS |

steve@stevennoble.com   direct: 707-789-0166   mobile: 415-897-6961   www.stevennoble.com

© 2014 - Boston Harbor Distillery

© Copyright 2014 - Desert Camel

© 2014 - Dairy Logo

© 2014 - Three Happy Cows

© 2014 - Cocoa Plants

© 2014 - Chicago Tribune Logo

ALABAMA GREAT SEAL

MAP OF ALABAMA

© Copyright 2014 - Lander Jenkins

World Class Illustrations from over 3,500 images and over 1,000 stock illustrations for clients from all over the world!

2006 Rosey Awards • Mead Show Award Winner 2001 • Brand New 2009 • Ad Pulp 2009 • Communications Arts 1997 • National Addy Awards 2010

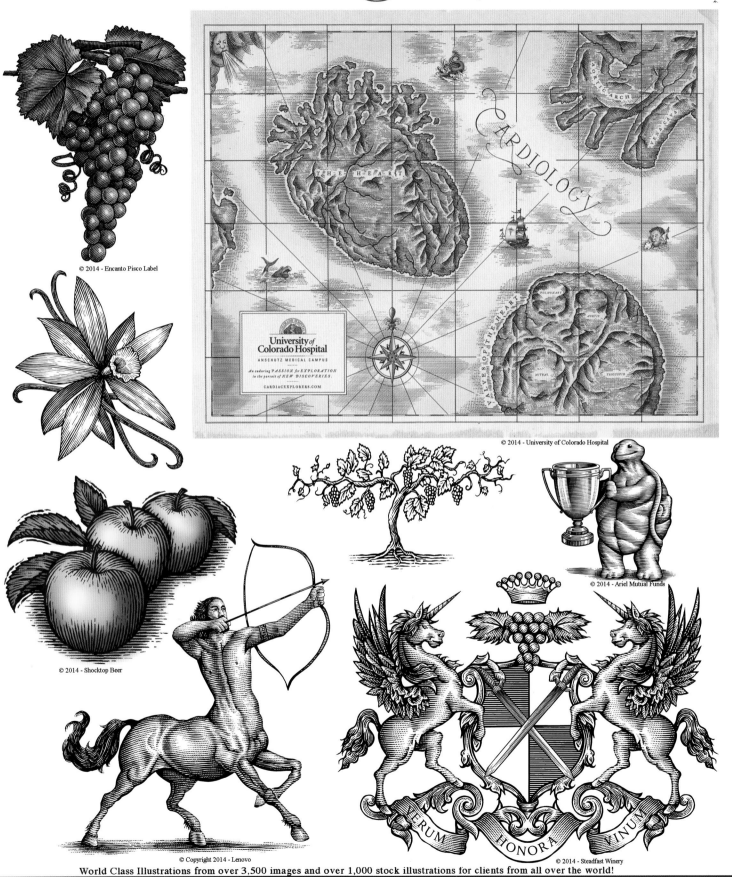

STEVEN NOBLE

| SCRATCHBOARD | LINE ART | ENGRAVINGS | WOODCUTS |

steve@stevennoble.com   direct: 707-789-0166   mobile: 415-897-6961   www.stevennoble.com

© 2014 - Encanto Pisco Label

University of
Colorado Hospital
ANSCHUTZ MEDICAL CAMPUS
An enduring PASSION for EXPLORATION
in the pursuit of NEW DISCOVERIES.
CARDIACEXPLORERS.COM

© 2014 - University of Colorado Hospital

© 2014 - Ariel Mutual Funds

© 2014 - Shocktop Beer

VERUM   HONORA   VINUM

© Copyright 2014 - Lenovo

© 2014 - Steadfast Winery

World Class Illustrations from over 3,500 images and over 1,000 stock illustrations for clients from all over the world!

2006 Rosey Awards • Mead Show Award Winner 2001 • Brand New 2009 • Ad Pulp 2009 • Communications Arts 1997 • National Addy Awards 2010

STEVEN NOBLE

| SCRATCHBOARD | LINE ART | ENGRAVINGS | WOODCUTS |

steve@stevennoble.com · direct: 707-789-0166 · mobile: 415-897-6961 · www.stevennoble.com

GULF OF MAINE

RESPONSIBLY HARVESTED

www.gmri.org

POUR LA PATRIE LES SCIENCES LA GLOIRE

© 2014 - Espolon Tequila

© Copyright 2014 - MVC Lions

© Copyright 2014 - Ecole Polytechnique Logo

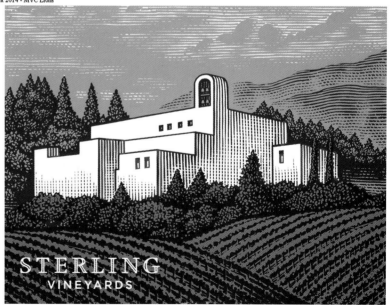

STERLING
VINEYARDS

© Copyright 2014 - Louis Armstrong

© Copyright 2014 - Sterling Vineyards

World Class Illustrations from over 3,500 images and over 1,000 stock illustrations for clients from all over the world!

2006 Rosey Awards · Mead Show Award Winner 2001 · Brand New 2009 · Ad Pulp 2009 · Communications Arts 1997 · National Addy Awards 2010

STEVEN NOBLE

| SCRATCHBOARD | LINE ART | ENGRAVINGS | WOODCUTS |

steve@stevennoble.com   direct: 707-789-0166   mobile: 415-897-6961   www.stevennoble.com

FAIRCHILD

G·III

CABERNET SAUVIGNON

2014

© 2014 - Fairchild Wines

EST. 1973

© 2014 - Kilbeggan Whiskey

ELEVEN
RESTAURANT

© Copyright 2014 - Williams Sonoma

© 2014 - Burt's Bees

© 2014 - The Tuna Store

World Class Illustrations from over 3,500 images and over 1,000 stock illustrations for clients from all over the world!

2006 Rosey Awards   •   Mead Show Award Winner 2001   •   Brand New 2009   •   Ad Pulp 2009   •   Communications Arts 1997   •   National Addy Awards 2010

Biological, scientific, and molecular art installations for public spaces, corporations, museums, interiors, and publications.

858 459-2773   •   linda@lsnye.com   •   www.patternofnature.com
For more illustration and animation visit: www.visualizingnature.com

Pattern of Nature . com
The art works of Linda S. Nye

Detail from Emory University mural.

FUN-1 Illustration & Design Studio

614-326-3861 • fun-1studio.com

Jan Benham, Illustrator

Alice Rebecca Potter
www.alicepotter.co.uk
+44(0)7816371892

DIANECARDACI.COM

302

GREG RUHL

gregruhl@mac.com   416 928 1997   gregruhl.com

Darren McKee • (214) 343-8766 • mckee1darren@hotmail.com • www.darrenmckeedraws.com

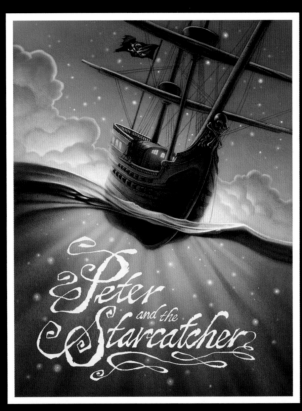

801.274.2407   gregnewbold.com

DANIEL LANDERMAN:
illustrator   www.ArtDL.com
storyteller   e: Daniel@ArtDL.com
art enthusiast   p: 707-694-8180

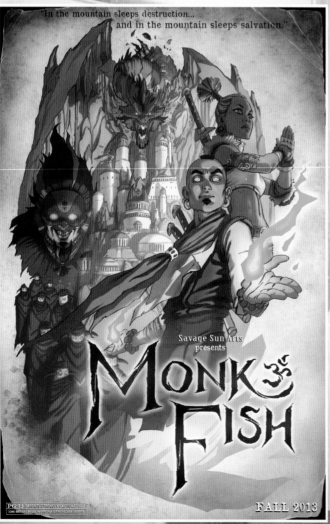

"In the mountain sleeps destruction...
and in the mountain sleeps salvation."

Savage Sun Arts
presents

MONK FISH

FALL 2013

Dakota Rawhide
Book 1

Written
an'
Rendered
by
Daniel Landerman

Jennifer Adejobi

www.jenniferadejobi.com
510.717.8844

307

(905) 876-2237
norm@normlanting.com   **www.normlanting.com**

Norm Lanting

Tara Garrigan

TaraGarrigan.com   912-441-6698   TaraGarrigan@me.com

The clock numbers read: 5, 4, 8, 9, 2, 6, 3, 7

Kim Smerek Illustration
www.kimsmerek.com 604-815-7937

Michael Grills Illustration Studio
www.michaelgrills.ca | art@michaelgrills.ca | 403 921 6112

ALICIA SEVERSON
Illustration & Design

aliciaseverson.com
alicia.k.severson@gmail.com
832.392.1014

ALICIA SEVERSON
Illustration & Design

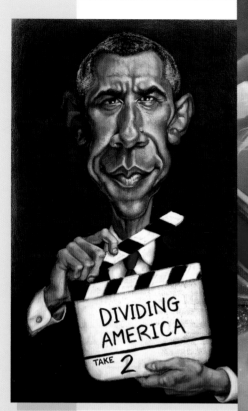

DIVIDING AMERICA

TAKE 2

BOSTON

Daniel Alsheimer
CARICATURE ILLUSTRATION   607.379.0928
WWW.DANIELALSHEIMER.COM

masapopo

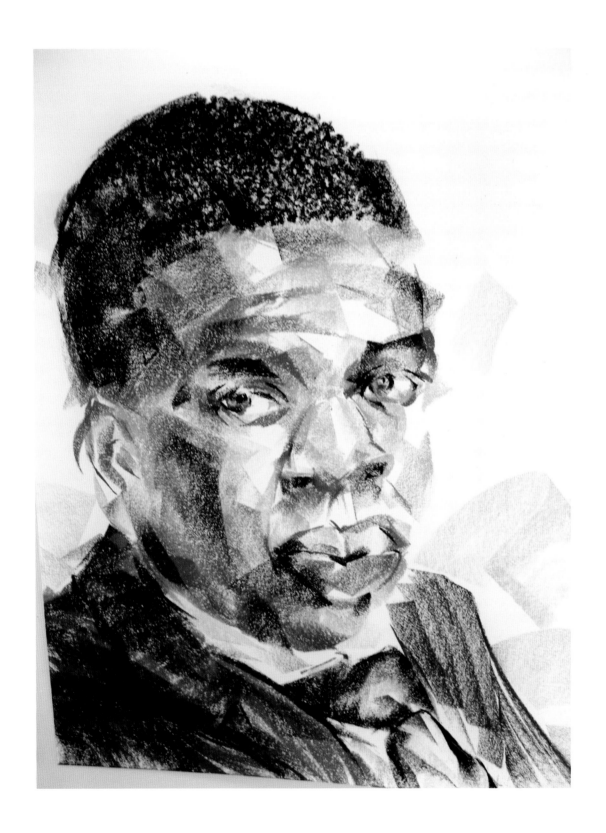

www.masapopo.com

Erwin Sherman
ILLUSTRATOR

ERWIN@ERWINSHERMAN.COM • (817)926-7299 • ERWINSHERMAN.COM

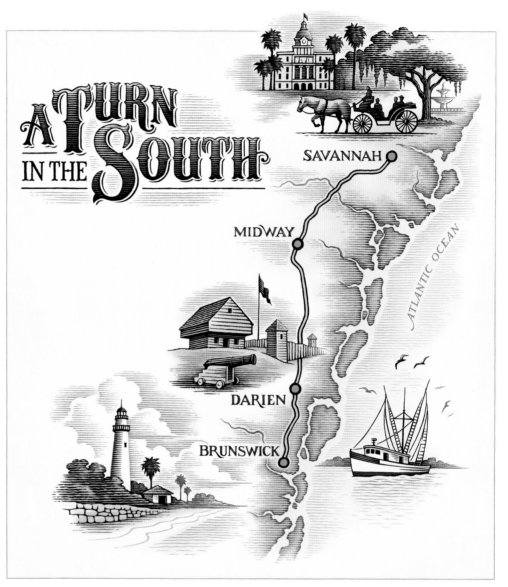

A TURN IN THE SOUTH

SAVANNAH

MIDWAY

DARIEN

BRUNSWICK

ATLANTIC OCEAN

FOR HIRE

ERWIN SHERMAN
ILLUSTRATOR

ERWIN@ERWINSHERMAN.COM   •   (817)926-7299   •   ERWINSHERMAN.COM

MARK BOARDMAN
Illustration

www.mark-boardman.com
mark@mark-boardman.com
+44 (0) 7527 563 974

TYLER ELLIS ILLUSTRATION

portfolio.tgellis.com   tyler@tgellis.com   (254) 366-6724

TYLER ELLIS ILLUSTRATION

portfolio.tgellis.com tyler@tgellis.com (254) 366-6724

WWW.BRUNSILLUSTRATION.COM
ALLISON@BRUNSILLUSTRATION.COM

503.789.3511

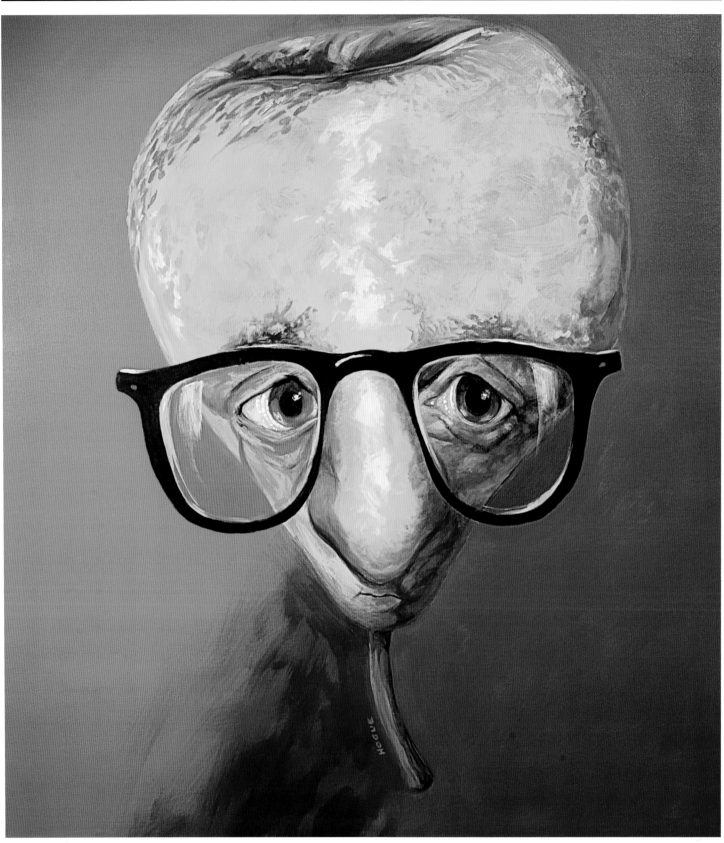

M   a   n   h   a   tt   a   n

TOM WHITE • 9 SURF STUDIOS • 212.866.8778 • 9SURF.COM

TOM WHITE • 9 SURF STUDIOS • 212.866.8778 • 9SURF.COM

RYAN HOBSON DESIGN

ILLUSTRATION • DESIGN • INTERACTIVE • PAPER ENGINEERING

© Smartlab Toys

© Scholastic Books

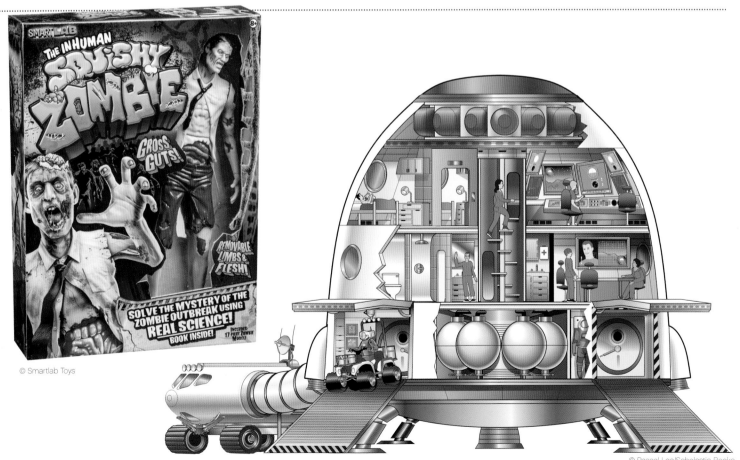

© Smartlab Toys

© Pascal Lee/Scholastic Books

www.ryanhobson.com   •   ryan@ryanhobson.com   •   206.354.3910

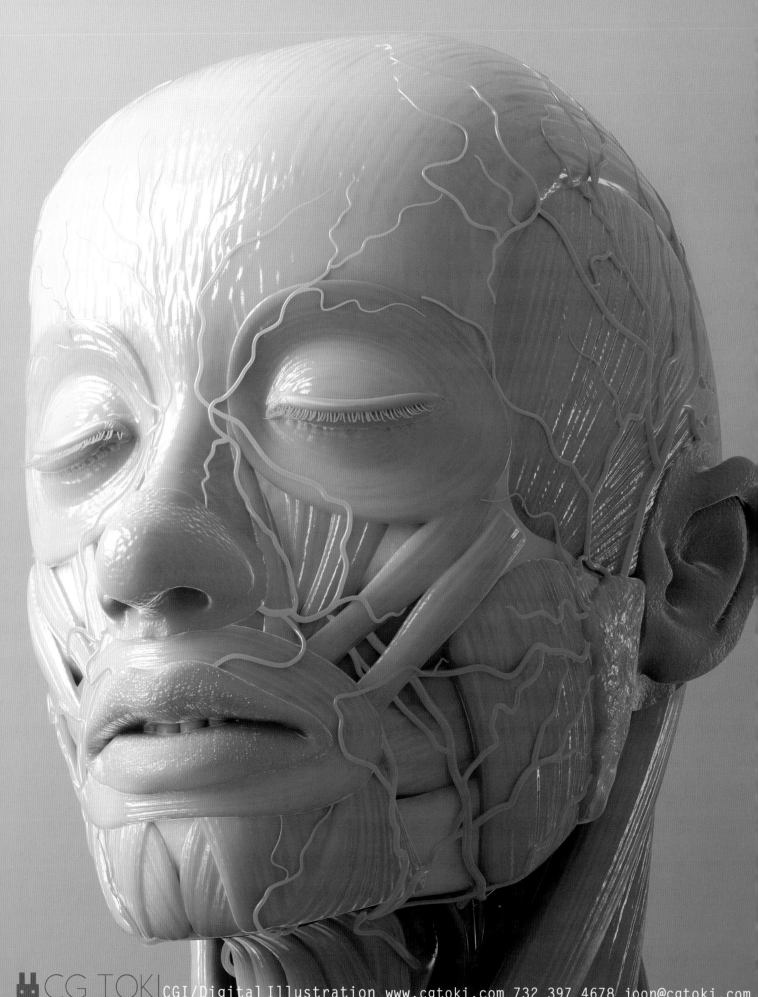

CG TOKI CGI/Digital Illustration www.cgtoki.com 732 397 4678 joon@cgtoki.com

RANDY FISHER
ILLUSTRATION

972.539.7697   mobile 214.663.1003   randy.fisher7@verizon.net   www.fisher-illustration.com

james mann art farm

www.jamesmannartfarm.com
jrm@jamesmannartfarm.com
610.965.8046

PETERIS LIDAKA
ILLUSTRATION & MODEL MAKING

www.peterislidaka.com | peteris@peterislidaka.com | +371 26558063

sawsanchalabi
design & illustration
703.589.5196 | sawsan@schalabi.com
www.schalabi.com

wesleybedrosian.com

718.614.9080 | **mail@wesleybedrosian.com**

Clients include: The New York Times, Barron's, Vanity Fair, Advertising Age, 8x8, Billboard Magazine, Fortune, Tennis Magazine, The Wall Street Journal, The Progressive, Time, Harvard Medical, Forbes, The Boston Globe, The Washington Post, New York Magazine, SmartMoney, The Nation

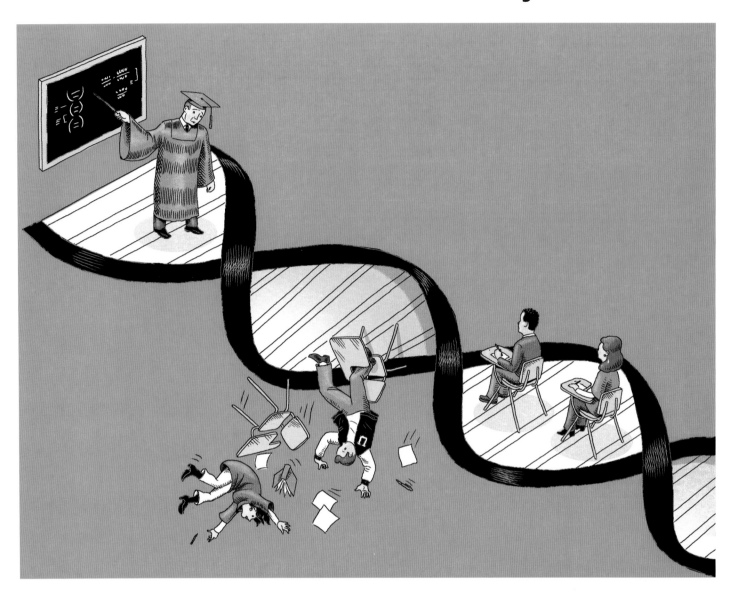

mail@wesleybedrosian.com | 718.614.9080

Clients include: The New York Times, Barron's, Vanity Fair, Advertising Age, 8x8, Billboard Magazine, Fortune, Tennis Magazine, The Wall Street Journal, The Progressive, Time, Harvard Medical, Forbes, The Boston Globe, The Washington Post, New York Magazine, SmartMoney, The Nation

Carolyn Ridsdale

www.carolynridsdale.com | e: carolyn@carolynridsdale.com | t: +61 4 504 89829

GENE MOLLICA

PHOTO-ILLUSTRATOR

www.genemollica.com | gene@genemollica.com | 201.216.1663

GENE MOLLICA

PHOTO–ILLUSTRATOR

www.genemollica.com | gene@genemollica.com | 201.216.1663

GREG PAPROCKI

GregPaprocki.com | Greg@GregPaprocki.com | 402.932.0722

© Greg Paprocki 2014

GREG PAPROCKI

GregPaprocki.com | Greg@GregPaprocki.com | 402.932.0722

© Greg Paprocki 2014

IllustratedMaps.com
RabinkyArt.com

info@rabinkyart.com   877-277-1768

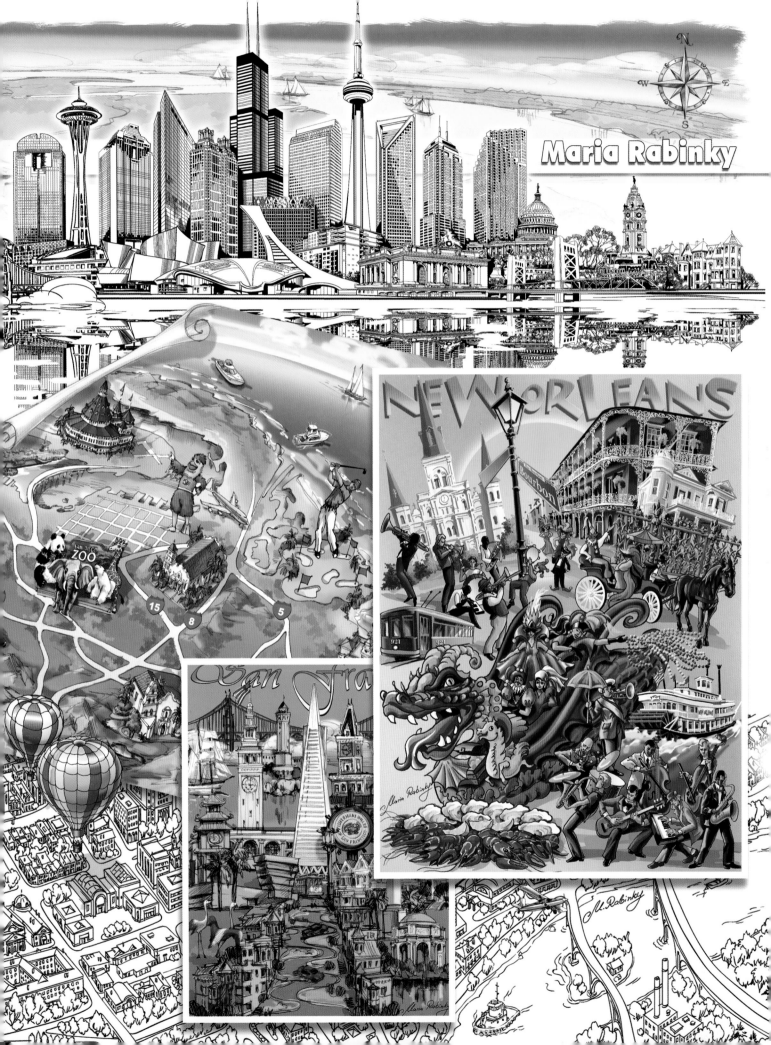

SACHA
TREAGER
ILLUSTRATOR
SACHAILLUSTRATES.COM

Maureen Edgecomb

TM CE, Inc.
© Maureen Edgecomb

Some images © Disney

Corey
Wolfe

360 8825397
www.coreywolfe.com

me images © Disney and Mattel

KRISTIN
ABBOTT
ILLUSTRATION
abbottillustration.com
650-740-3669
kma@abbott1.com

Terry Paczko   216 447 8864   terrypaczko@ameritech.net   terrypaczko.com

Lesley Wolf

Illustration **W** *Design*

wolfdesigns@cox.net • www.lesleywolf.com • 805.962.6621

LAUREN J BRADING   OFFTHEPAGEDESIGN.COM

PHONE 774 368 0224   SKYPE   LINKEDIN   LAUREN@OFFTHEPAGEDESIGN.COM

amyGrogan
Traditional Linocuts

amyagrogan@gmail.com 970.799.2469 amyagrogan.com

Lupine

advertising

editorial

packaging

books

354

Simple eloquent illustrations
to engage, inspire and entertain.

Dave Cutler

davecutlerstudio.com

203 938 7067

Jacqueline East Illustration
www.jacquelineeast.com
info@jacquelineeast.com
+44 117 904822

PETER BREESE   PETERBREESE.COM   303-842-3041

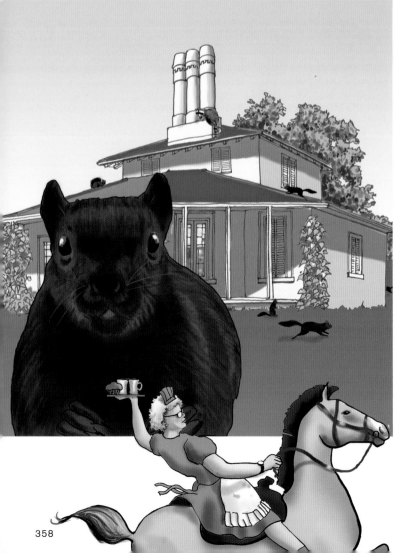

Steve Yeates 416-531-575

358

Bay and Gable

Arts and Crafts

Workers C

steve@steveyeates.ca   www.steveyeates.ca

each FLOWER & HERB on earth's dark breast ROSE FROM THE DREAMS of its W!NTRY REST

— Percy Bysshe Shelley

THANK YOU

ANNI BETTS
illustration

anni@annibetts.com
ANNIBETTS.COM
312.212.3375 US
07462 180 348 UK

Pam Little, CMI

Specialized Illustration
PLLC

plittle@montana.com
406 961 3523

http://www. directory of Illustration.com
http://pam-little.squarespace.com

KEN TACKETT

KenTackett@Suddenlink.net
www.KenTackettart.com
603-724-7995

Frog knew that her friend wasn't feeling so swell, so she gave her coloring books and crayons to wish her well.

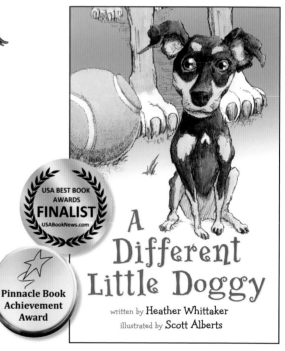

A Different Little Doggy

written by Heather Whittaker
illustrated by Scott Alberts

USA BEST BOOK AWARDS FINALIST
USABookNews.com

Pinnacle Book Achievement Award

ALBERTS
ILLUSTRATION & DESIGN

Scott Alberts Illustration & Design

920.277.1425 · scott@scottalberts.com · www.scottalberts.com

— Realism in Pen & Ink —

Scott Alberts Illustration & Design

920.277.1425 · scott@scottalberts.com · www.scottalberts.com

ALBERTS
ILLUSTRATION & DESIGN

WHO ARE YOU?

Survey results hold a mirror to our readers.

In November, Erdos & Morgan conducted an extensive survey by mail of IBM Systems Magazine subscribers. The 195 respondents from a random pool of recipients illuminate a portrait of our readers. Where do you rank compared with your peers?

Readers' Companies

Manufacturing (92.8% computer related)
22.3%

10.4% Banking & Financial Services

9.3% Wholesale Distribution

7.3% Insurance

6.7% Retail

6.2% Government / Military

4.7% Consultant

4.1% Agriculture, Mining or Construction

3.6% Education

3.6% Hospital / Medical

3.6% Software Developer and/or Sales

3.6% Transportation

3.1% Computer Dealer / Reseller

2.6% Telecommunications

8.7% Other

READERS
86.8 % male
Average age 53
Average income $106,300

Readers' Positions

IT Management
43.4%

IT Staff 19.2%

Executive Management (CEO, President, VP) 17.1%

General / Corporate Manager or Director 7.8%

Systems Analyst / Program Management 7.8%

Consultant 1.6%

LAN/ Network Management 1.6%

Sales Marketing Management 1.0%

Reseller / Distributor .5%

neilstewart.net
illustration • information • imagination

telephone: (416) 516-3535 • email: studio@neilstewart.net • folio: www.neilstewart.net

neilstewart.net
illustration • information • imagination

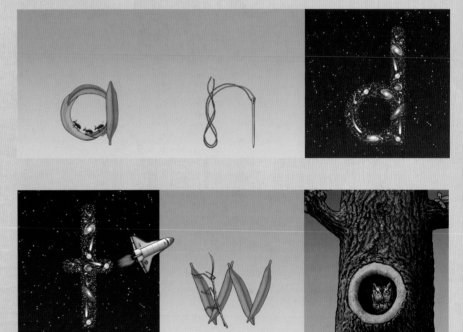

Leslie Arwin
734.330.4430
leslie@arwin.net

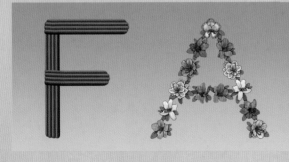

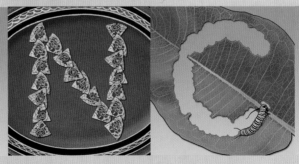

Illustrations: www.lesliearwin.com   IOS apps: www.alphabetgalleries.com

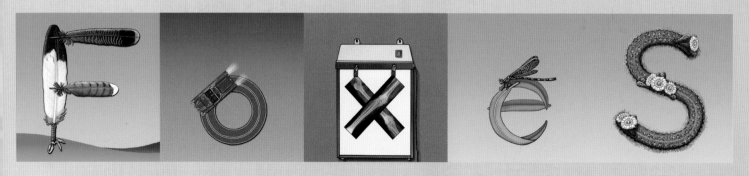

Leslie Arwin   Contact: leslie@arwin.net   734.330.4430

Janet Allinger Design
Graphic Designer & Illustrator Specializing in :
Wine Labels, Logos, Posters & More!

CONTACT ME →

JEFF GRUNEWALD
DIGITAL ILLUSTRATION

773-281-5284

WWW.JEFFGRUNEWALD.COM

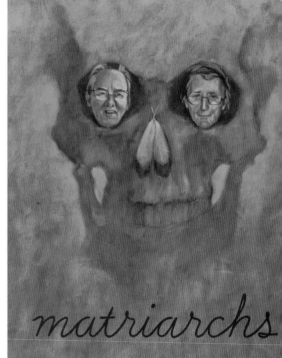

HUGH DUNNAHOE

HUGH.DUNNAHOE@DUNNAHOE.COM

501-624-6200

Nicole Allin

708·337·1939

allinart@fastmail.fm

www.allinart.net

faye@fayewilson.com fayewilson.com

VI PHAM

ILLUSTRATION & CONCEPT ART

www.vidraws.com / vidraws@gmail.com / 619.723.7557

GATIS SLUKA

www.gatissluka.com
gatis@karikatura.lv

f /karikaturalv
@karikaturalv

illustrations · cartoons · caricatures · animations

Vanessa Wright

t. + 61 (02) 9 340 1448
m.+ 61 0450 022 782
vanessa@vanessawright.com
www.vanessawright.com

Award winning illustrator with international
client base. Specializing in iconic, contemporary,
corporate and packaging illustration.

www.illustrationlives.com ~ JAMES GOODRIDGE ILLUSTRATION ~ (626)576-7293

Windows to the Artist's World

Paula Wallace Studios
Hot Shops Art Center, Omaha, Nebraska

paulawallacefineart.com
+1 773.750.2263

The Red Shoes

Megan Johnson
artist • illustrator

434.221.8106
twitter @meganartwork

meganjohnsonartwork.com
info@meganjohnsonartwork.com

DARYLL✿DARYLLCOLLINS.COM

• ADVERTISING • EDITORIAL
• PUBLISHING • PACKAGING
• CHARACTER DESIGN

VG WAYMER ILLUSTRATION

. www.vgwaymer.com . veedraws@gmail.com . (757)971-2735 .

NEPENTHEAN.COM
DESIGN & ILLUSTRATION
M: 1.347.239.5679 • KCOTREMBA@GMAIL.COM

casey otremba

Marina Micheli **Studio**
www.marinamichelistudio.com
marinamicheliart@gmail.com
tel. 001.212.533.7639

marina micheli
STUDIO
tel. 001.212.533.7639
marinamicheliart@gmail.com
www.marinamichelistudio.com

Images that inform...explain the concept visually...transform complexity into clarity.

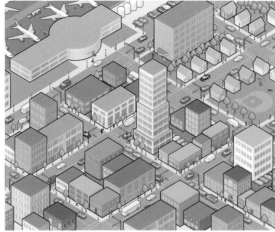
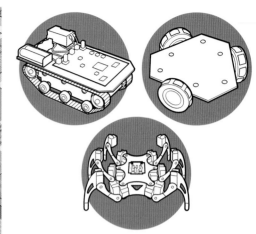

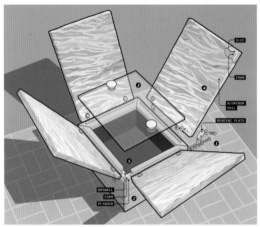

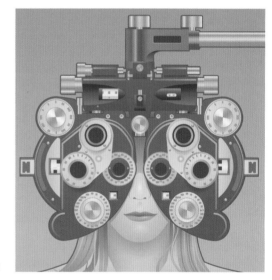

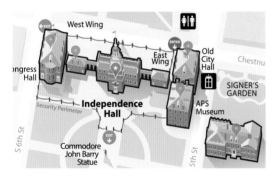

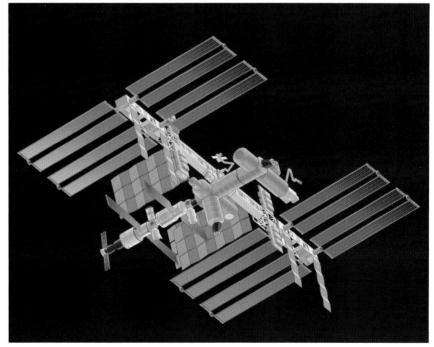

vic@vickulihinillustration.com ▪ 908.757.4678 ▪ www.vickulihinillustration.com

Fiona Sansom
Illustration

email@fionasansom.com
www.fionasansom.com
+44 (0)20 8840 2783

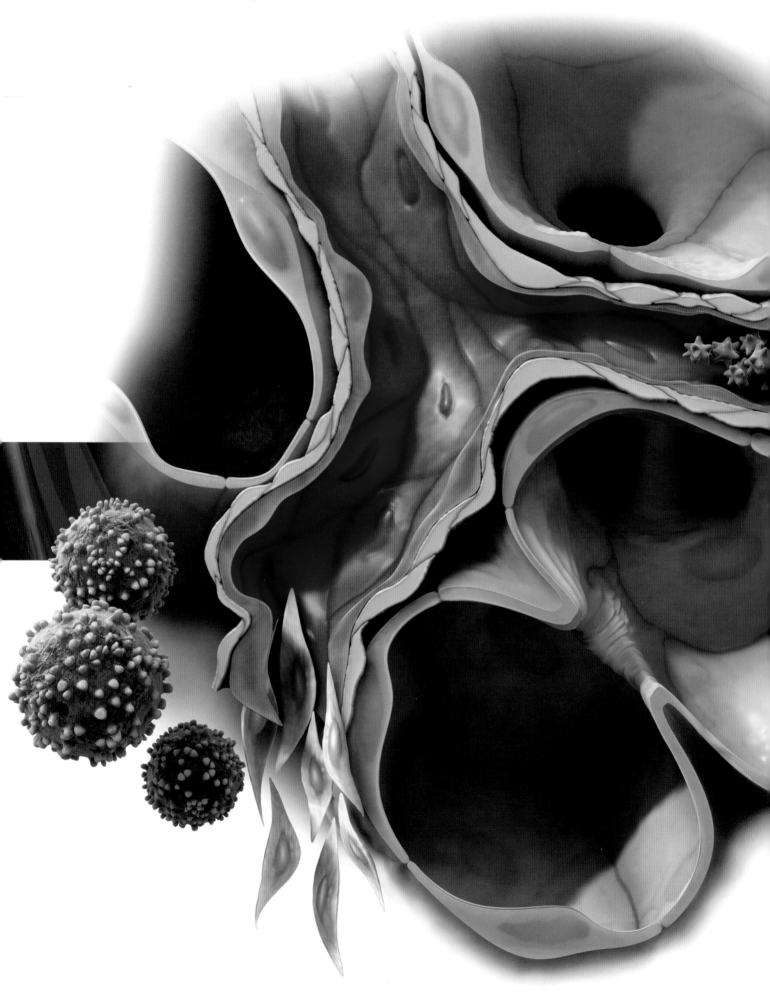

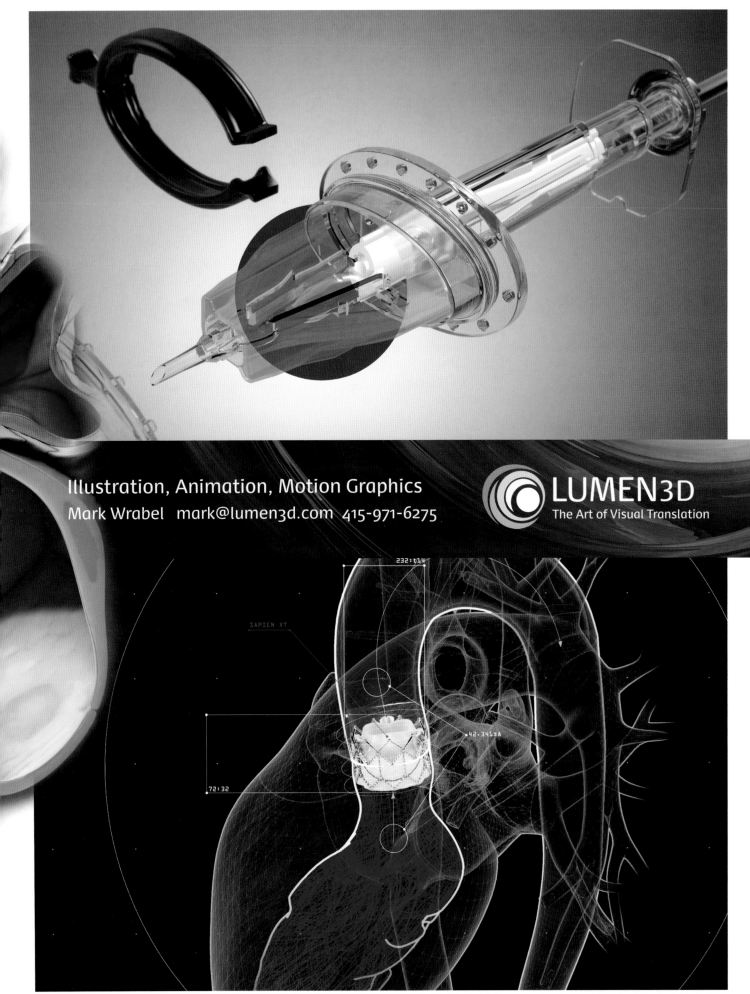

Illustration, Animation, Motion Graphics
Mark Wrabel   mark@lumen3d.com   415-971-6275

LUMEN3D
The Art of Visual Translation

SAPIEN XT

232:614

42-341±A

72:32

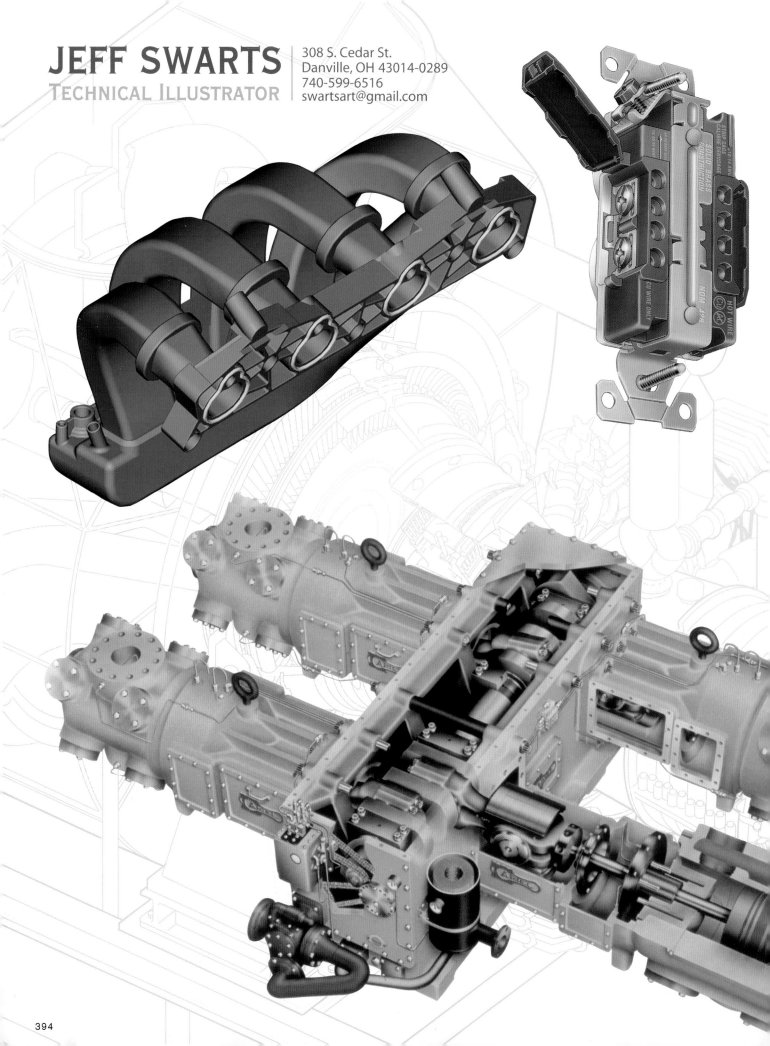

JEFF SWARTS
TECHNICAL ILLUSTRATOR

308 S. Cedar St.
Danville, OH 43014-0289
740-599-6516
swartsart@gmail.com

carlabauerdesign.

WOODCUT ILLUSTRATION

CARLAJBAUER@GMAIL.COM

646.335.5202

WWW.CARLABAUERDESIGN.COM

AMERICAN GAS
MAGAZINE

VARIETY

NATIONAL GEOGRAPHIC TRAVELER

THE NEW YORK TIMES

THE NEW YORK TIMES

FORBES

THE BOSTON GLOBE

HITZ-ILLUSTRATION.COM
(845) 626 7730

DAVE MURRAY　　　　**WWW.DAVEMURRAYILLUSTRATION.COM**　　　　**416.629.1717**

Catherine Weyerhaeuser

www.CWMdesigns.com

cathy@CWMdesigns.com

Blot Line

Blot Line is loose and loopy, thick/thin

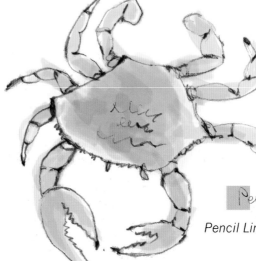

Pen Line

Pen Line is thin and crisp

Pencil Line

Pencil Line is sketchy/artsy

Brush Line

Brush Line is loose and energetic

Wiggle Line

Wiggle Line is fun and wiggley

mary Ross

ILLUSTRATION

Mary Ross works in 5 distinct styles, all with her signiture "Less is More" ability to reduce form to essence.

maryrossillustration.com   415 661·2930

Dungeness Crab

400

ILLUSTRATION

One illustrator, 5 unique styles, many subjects, (including caricatures), all with her signature ability to reduce form to essence.

maryrossillustration.com   415 661·2930

Blot Line

Blot Line is loose and loopy, thick/thin

Pencil Line

Pencil Line is sketchy/artsy

Brush Line

Brush Line is loose and energetic

Wiggle Line

Wiggle Line is fun and wiggley

Pen Line

Pen Line is thin and crisp

925-890-7037   Milena Konukova   www.milenakonukova.com

The Art of McKeever Jeffrey B.

❋ JEFFREY B. MCKEEVER 908.763.2798 SCREAMINGCELT@VERIZON.NET SCREAMINGCELTSTUDIO.COM ❋

ILLUSTRATION ❖ FANTASY ❖ SCI-FI ❖ SOCIAL COMMENTARY

EVE STECCATI
PICTORIAL MAPS

PHONE: 510.339.0182   PORTFOLIO: stcreative.com/eve.html   EMAIL: eve@stcreative.com

REGENERATED ART STUDIOS | PORTRAIT ILLUSTRATION
REGENERATEDARTS.COM   267-585-2415   REGENERATED.ART@ GMAIL.COM

Mark Evan Walker Illustration

817.905.0057
email: markart@hush.com
folio: markevanwalker.com

dennis wunsch illustration   denniswunsch.com   425.984.4374

dennis wunsch illustration   denniswunsch.com   425.984.4374

Derek Douglas

w: www.rightsidestudios.com
e: rightsidestudios@me.com
t: 2 8 9 . 2 4 2 . 3 8 0 4

RIGHT SIDE STUDIOS ILLUSTRATION

Derek Douglas

w: www.rightsidestudios.com
e: rightsidestudios@me.com
t: 289.242.3804

RIGHT SIDE STUDIOS ILLUSTRATION

THE ARTWORK OF
BRIAN
·DEMETER·
WWW.BRIANDEMETER.COM

Sarah Wisbey

FRESH ILLUSTRATION
SERVED DAILY

sarah@wisbeydesign.com   wisbeydesign.com

www.STEPHANHERR.com | 717.426.2939 | tad@stephanherr.com

JOHN MANTHA

416 778 5089

john.mantha@sympatico.ca

johnmantha.com

JESSICA LeCLERC

www.jessicaleclerc.com
jesskleclerc@gmail.com
603.703.1994

c R o d *Illustration*

Alfred the Alligator ate absolutely anything, except he was actually allergic to Apricots.

Christina Ann Rodriguez

t: (732) 580.4301
w: www.crodillustration.com
e: mail@crodillustration.com

[advertising]

[books]

[magazines]

[games]

kevin kelly
illustrations
972+814+0690

professorjunk.com   +   rtbrain@pixelpushersdesign.com

972-491-6779 **ROBERT L. PRINCE** robertlprince.com

420

mylestalbot.com

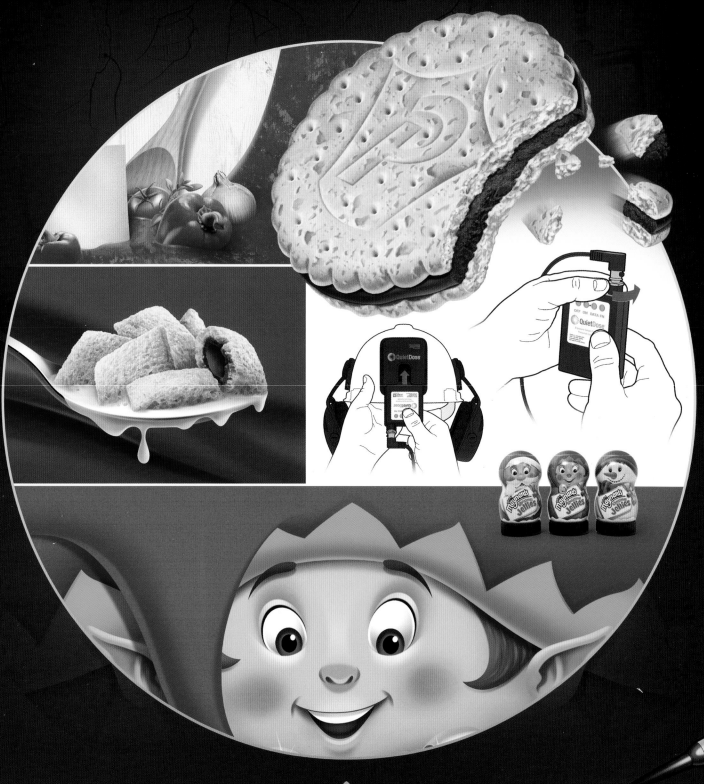

THE ENGLISH
SUMMER BERRY Cº

EVERY BERRY PROUDLY GROWN IN ENGLAND

studio@mylestalbot.com

+44 (0) 1274 510338

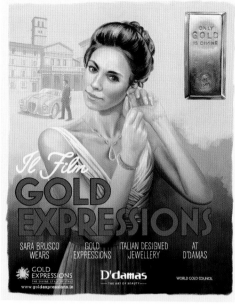

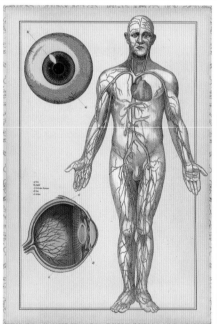

BOB VENABLES

www.bobvenables.co.uk   robert.venables1@btopenworld.com   +44 (0)1983 562321

CORNEL RUBINO

ILLUSTRATION MURALS FINE ART | CORNEL-RUBINO.COM 410.908.7797 CORNELRUBINO@GMAIL.COM | COMMUNICATION ARTS ILLUSTRATION ANNUAL

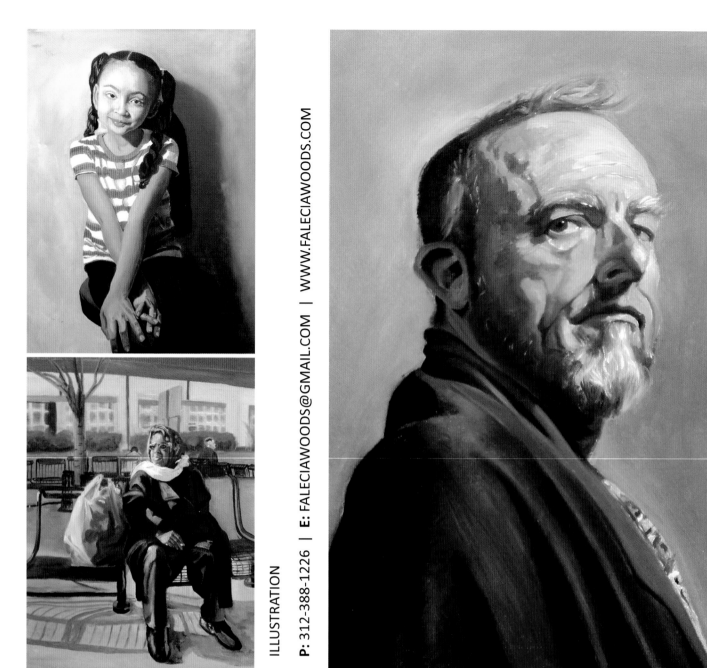

FALECIA WOODS

ILLUSTRATION

P: 312-388-1226 | **E:** FALECIAWOODS@GMAIL.COM | WWW.FALECIAWOODS.COM

BILBAO

JAN MURPHY

murphyartworks.com
jan.murphy@mac.com
650.207.8395

Steve Bjorkman

stevebjorkman.com   stevebjorkman@sbcglobal.net
949-349-0109

Steve Bjorkman

stevebjorkman.com   stevebjorkman@sbcglobal.net
949-349-0109

431

JUCUNDUS

ORANGE HONEY WHEAT

CLARITAS

KÖLSCH

GRAZIAS

VIENNA CREAM ALE

Creatures, logos and packaging
designed for Mike Hess Brewing
of San Diego

patton brothers
illustration & design, inc.

619.463.4562

pattonbros.com

pattonbros@cox.net

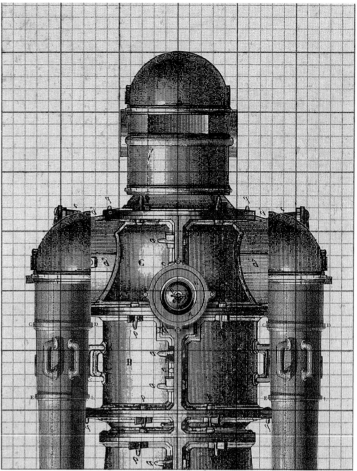

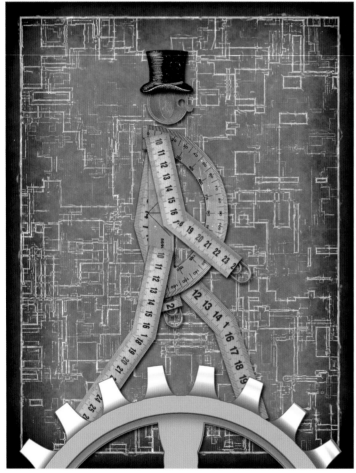

JIM COHEN ILLUSTRATION 847-726-8979

www.jimcohenillustration.com

Prespa Studios©

Petre Paspalovski
www.prespastudios.com • ppaspal@prespastudios.com • 330-342-1611

Linda Howard Bittner

Wild Graphics Studio
1908 Compton Road
Cincinnati, Ohio 45231
513-600-1955
wildgraphicsstudio@yahoo.com
lindahowardbittner.com

Member:
GNSI & SCBWI

Specializing in Nature & Wildlife Subjects

*Exhibits, Publishing, Licensing, Murals
Advertising, Product Developement,
Toys-Games, Graphic Design*

Clients Include:

National Geographic Books
National Arbor Day Foundation
Scholastic
McGraw-Hill
Wild Ohio Magazine
International Playthings
Bass Pro Shops
Oxford University Press
Hartz Mountain Pet Supplies
John James Audubon Museum
& Nature Center
Cincinnati Zoo & Botanical Gardens
Columbus Zoo & Aquarium
Izaak Walton League of America
Cincinnati Nature Center
Golden Books
North Light Books
Tree Stand Toys

JOHN F. MARTIN

MARTELLOSCREEN@GMAIL.COM

518-785-4796
518-701-3940

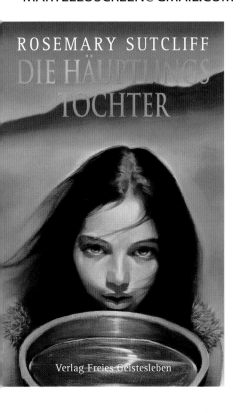

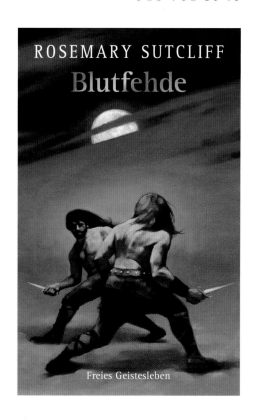

Morgan Spicer • MorSpicer@gmail.com
www.MorganSpicerIllustration.com

WILD

Classy

★
KENNETH THOMAS
Hyper-Active Creative Mind

PHONE: 215.8478341 ★ Ⓦ kenithomas.wordpress.com
Ⓘ @thomcat23 ★ ⓣ thomcat23.tumblr.com ★ Ⓨ @thomcat23tweets

Dan Rosandich
WWW.DANSCARTOONS.COM
dan@danscartoons.com

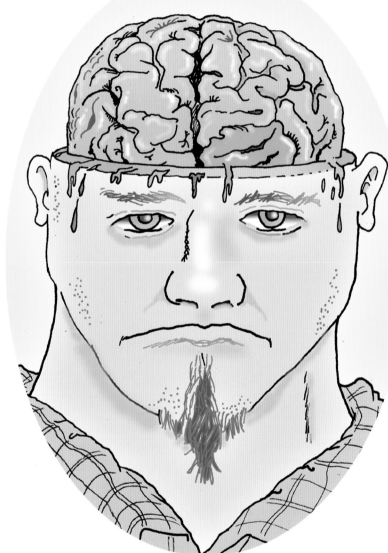

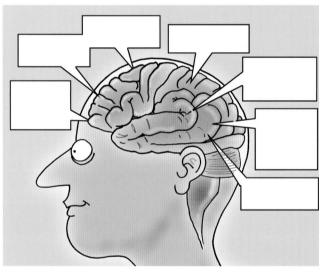

DEB MARVIN

GREY BLACKWELL

PRESIDENT PUTIN

SPORTS ON EARTH

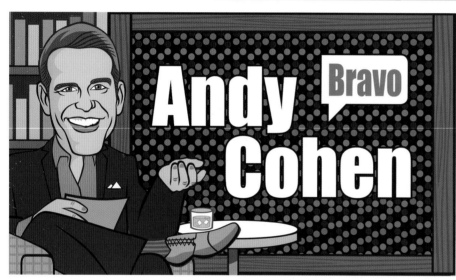

Andy Cohen

Bravo

portfolio
www.greyblackwell.com

call
919-693-1289

email
grey@greyblackwell.com

OF COURSE

442

barbara  kelley

631.754.7374 | www.barbarakelley.com | bkelley.art@gmail.com

Cheryl Orsini

Baguette

corsini01@optusnet.com.au • (61) 2 9314 1719 • cherylorsini.com • cherylorsiniillustration.blogspot.com.au

LANDIS • BLAIR

Landisblair@gmail.com • 815-793-4368 • www.Landisblair.com

Chellie Carroll Illustration

+44 (0) 7776 130790 chellie@chelliecarroll.co.uk www.chelliecarroll.co.uk

lynnefoster Imagine....

Illustration ■ motion ■ multimedia

lynnefoster@mac.com
mobile 212.996.2136
http://altpick.com/lynnfoster
http://www.directoryofillustration.com/
ArtistPortfolioThumbs.aspx?AID=6600

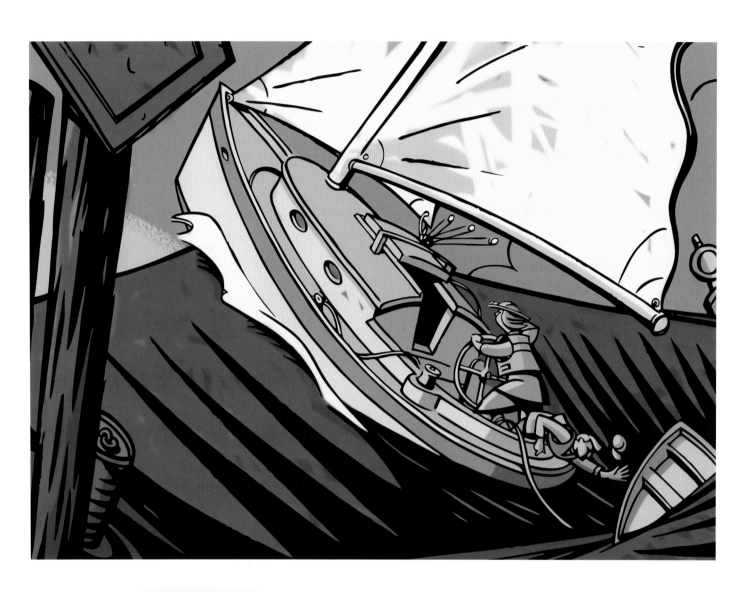

KIM LaFAVE ILLUSTRATION

604-885-0212   kimlafave.com

www.leohartas.com

LEO HARTAS
0044 (0)1823 672997

leo@leohartas.com

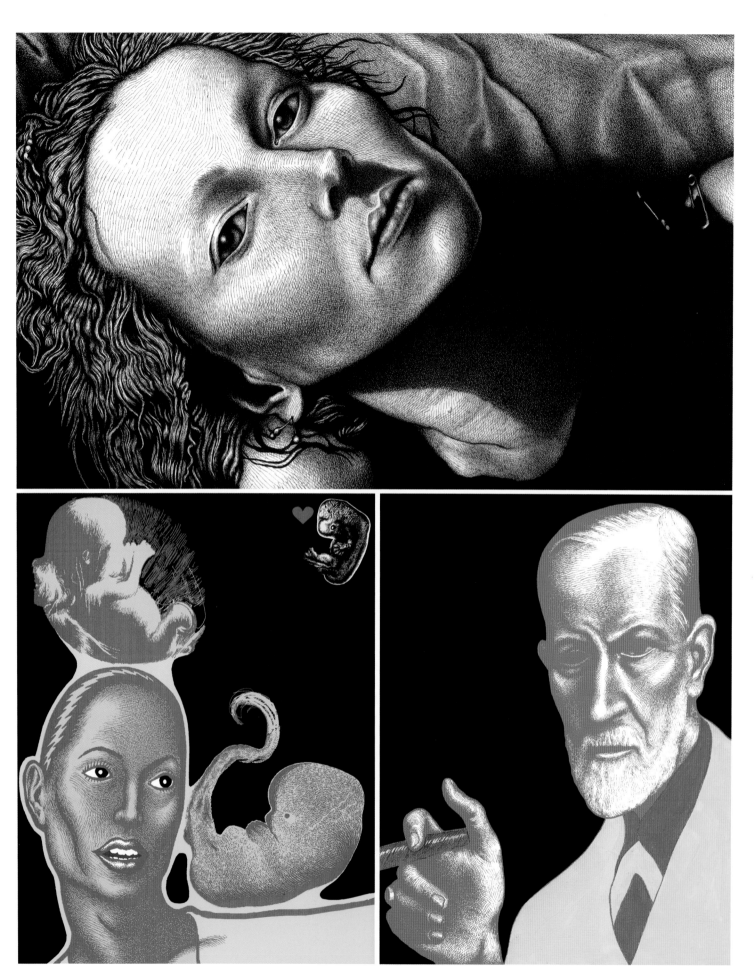

Jeffrey Katrencik

724-745-4577 katrencik@verizon.net http://www.katrencik.com

DAVID DeGranD

(817) 629-1930
mdaviddegrand@gmail.com
www.degrandland.com

Clients include:
MAD Magazine,
Nickelodeon,
MTV,
Harper Collins,
Bongo Comics,
Boom! Studios

STEPHEN HAIGH

illustration

www.stephenhaigh.com

267.278.3245

MARTY BEE ILLUSTRATION

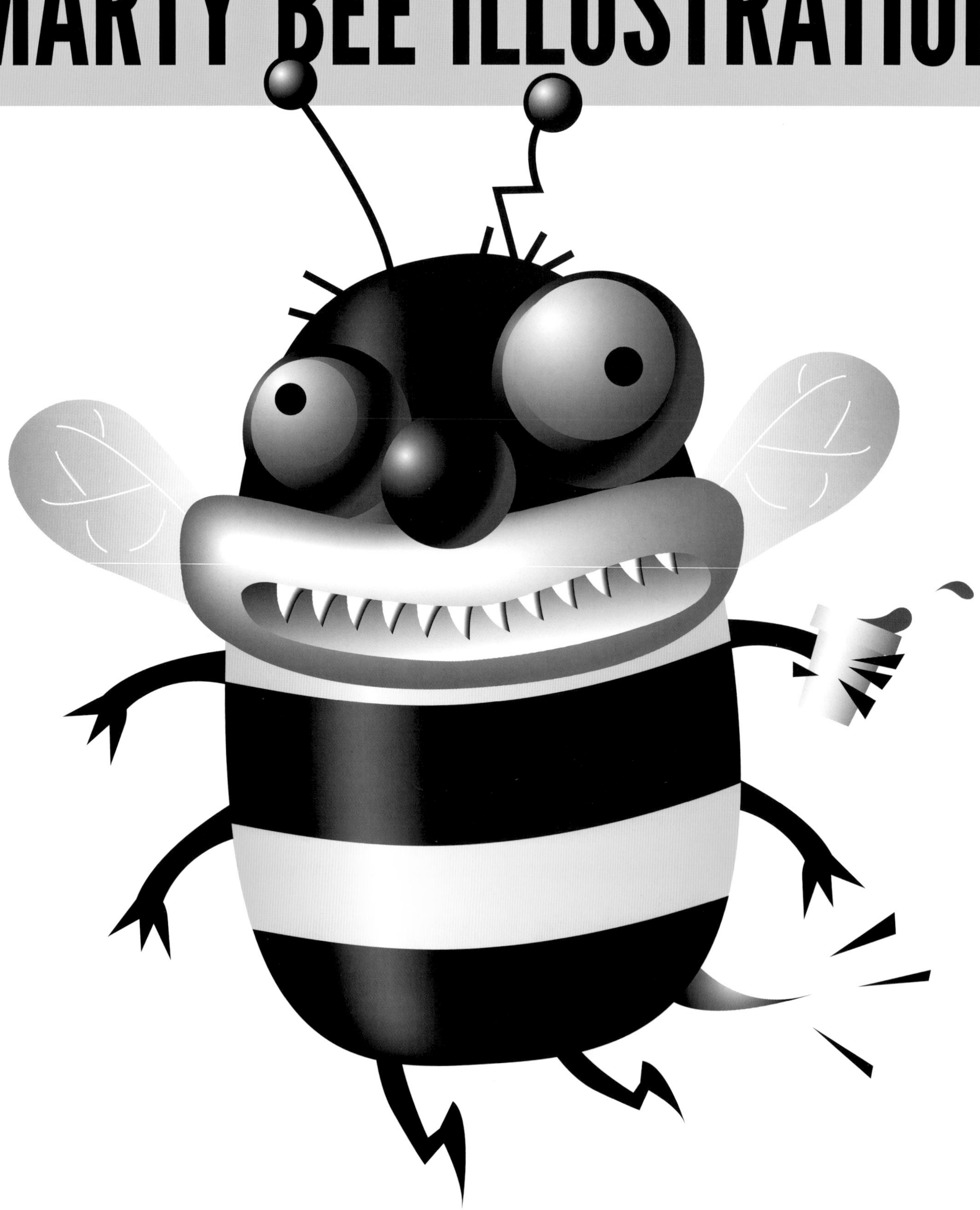

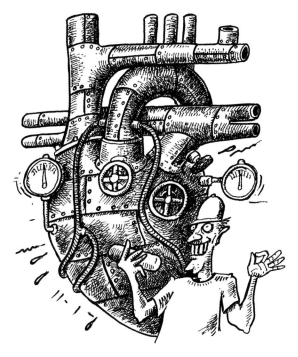

ILLUSTRATION
ANIMATION

marty@martybee.com
martybee.com
land line: 337.583.7715
cell: 337.563.9368

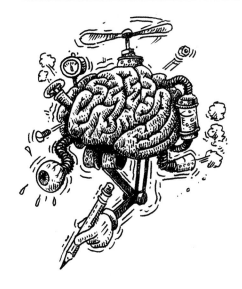

brian d. payne illustrator
brianpaynestudio.com
814.774.2812

Dino Pai
http://dinopai.com
dino@dinopai.com
604-726-5878

MELISSA DEHNER
HoneyBee Creative, LLC

913.449.9563
WWW.HONEYBEECREATIVE.NET
MELISSA@HONEYBEECREATIVE.NET

JIM ATHERTON • 702.401.6973 • www.AthertonCustoms.com

A—B

I'M SELLING COLORS®

WWW.ADHEMAS.COM

HELLO@ADHEMAS.COM

+1 310 893 4974

Matthew Johnson   MJillustration.com   Mjohns84@gmail.com

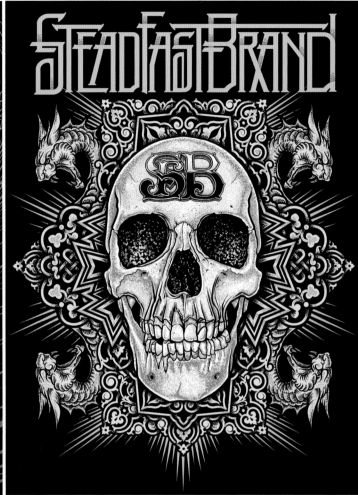

palehorse

portfolio:
palehorsedesign.com

email:
chris@palehorsedesign.com

phone:
727-823-6202

contact:
chris parks

MAGHEN BROWN

WWW.MAGHENBROWN.COM

MAGHEN@AOL.COM

914-466-5936

Baird Hoffmire
bairdhoffmire.com

TOM CHITTY drawnbytom.com +1 (647) 389 6986

TOM CHITTY drawnbytom.com +1 (647) 389 6986

Maury Aaseng

mauryillustrates.com
mauryillustrates@gmail.com
218-464-0189

ILLUSTRATION

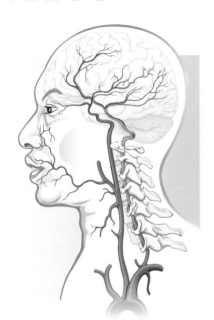

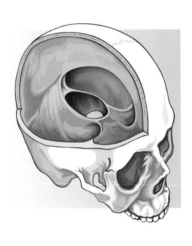

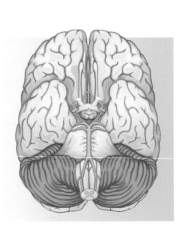

Anatomical   Watercolor   Informational   Technical   Cartoons   How to Draw

Yohey Horishita

www.yoheyhorishita.com

Copyright © Dayal Studio Inc. All Rights Reserved

ANTAR DAYAL STUDIO

805.895.8295
www.dayalstudio.com
www.antardayal.com

JoannaViheria

phone +44 777 149 9534   joannaviheria@gmail.com   http://joannaviheria.tumblr.com

john stanko

stankoillustration.com | 308.627.4832 | john@stankoillustration.com

concept art • cover art • fantasy and sci fi • historical illustrations

stankoillustration.com | 308.627.4832 | john@stankoillustration.com

iLLUSTRATiOn

gtownswick@yahoo.com

Gary Townswick
Illustration & Design

PH = 402-250-6758

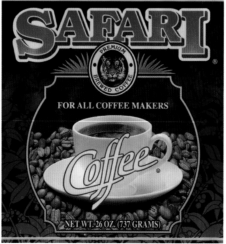

URL = garytownswick.wix.com/gt-design

I just want to do God's will.
And he's allowed me to go up to the mountain.
And I've looked over.
And I've seen the promised land.
I may not get there with you.
But I want you to know, that we,
will get to the promised land.
And I am happy, tonight.
I'm not worried about anything.
I'm not fearing any man.
Mine eyes have seen the glory
of the coming of the Lord.

BenJam'N Vincent

Illustration
Caricatures

Benvincent.com
ben.vincent@me.com
214 521-4904

c. delorenzo | WWW.CHRISDELORENZO.COM | @CHRISDELORENZO | CMDELORE@GMAIL.COM

DAVID K. ROSE * GRFXMONKEY

WWW.GRFXMONKEY.COM • DAVE@GRFXMONKEY.COM • (919) 389 - 2806

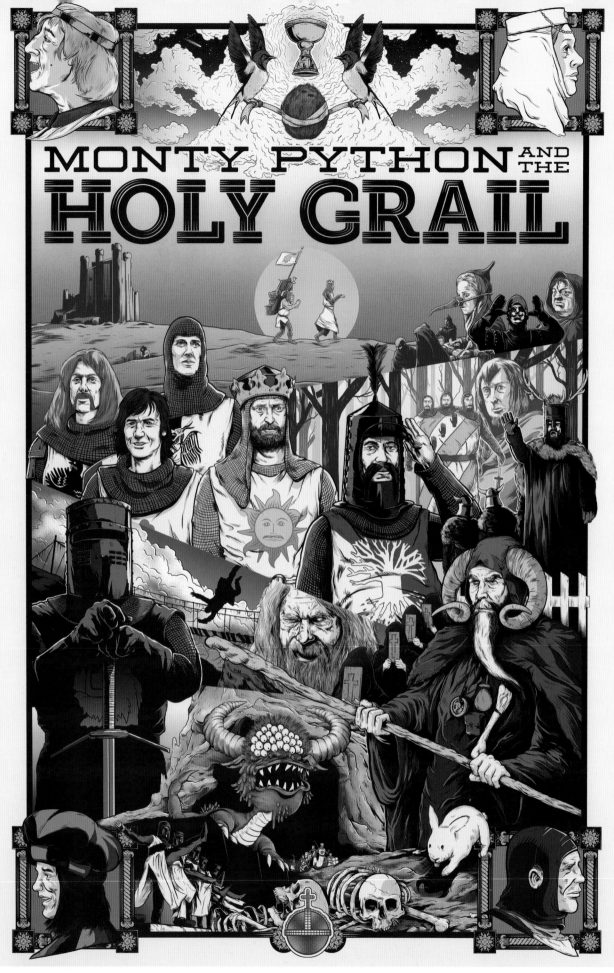

Nicholas Roberts
Nikoby Illustration & Design

NIKOBY.COM

(772) 913-4111
nroberts@nikoby.com

MUSTARD AND BOLONEY CARTOONS
www.mustardandboloney.com

Keywords: cartoons / illustration / character design / children books / graphic novels / caricature / editorial / storyboard / stories / scenario / plays / banners / postcards / gawns / animation / game design / motion design

client : Vling

Master chefs Jeffrey Caulfield and Alexandre Rouillard (aka Mustard and Boloney), are the only team to bring you an exotic and irresistible array of fine menu offerings; signature dishes that include: illustrations, cartoons, editorial panels, animation , and character design. Each meal is made utilizing only the finest and freshest ingredients available. Rest assured our food is never re-heated, recycled or microwaved. We simply guarantee to tantalize your palette, inspire your senses, and fill ones' stomach sans indigestion. Bon appetit!

client : Domnizelles

Le manteau, graphic novel
publisher: Mécanique générale

c/o Jeffrey Caulfield
& Alexandre Rouillard
47 Epsom Avenue Toronto
Ontario Canada M4C 2A8
Tel.: (416) 422-3667
Info@mustardandboloney.com

www.jimstarr.com   717-993-6598   jim@jimstarr.com

Jim Starr
illustration

"Handcrafted colored line art for today's digital world"

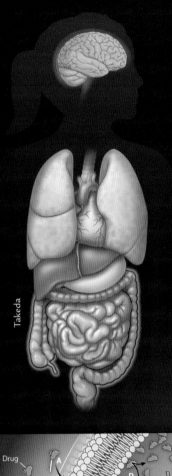
Takeda

Janssen

Science Magazine

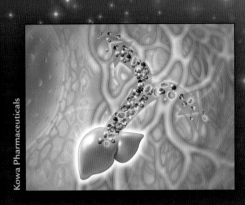
Kowa Pharmaceuticals

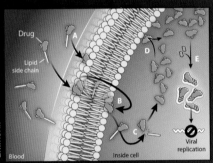
Chimerix

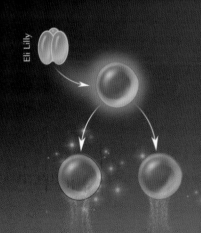
Eli Lilly

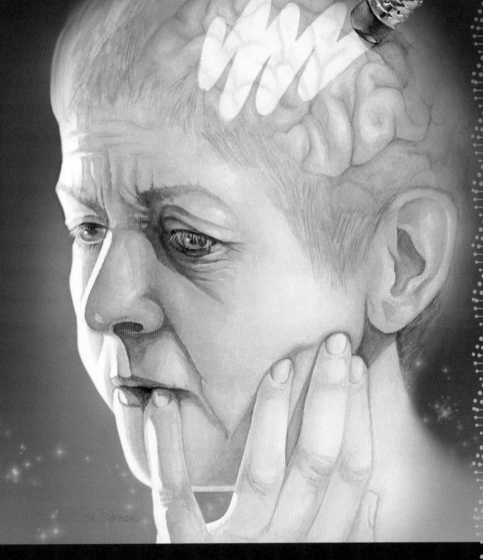

Lundbeck

ARTISTIC COMMUNICATION OF COMPLEX BIOMEDICAL CONCEPTS

BOARD CERTIFIED MEDICAL ILLUSTRATOR **MICA DURAN STUDIO**
The ART of SCIENCE.

1-800-493-4553 • *info@micaduran.com* • *www.micaduran.com*

All images © Mica Duran. All rights reserved.

NANU ILLUSTRATION

NANU ILLUSTRATION SPECIALIZES IN VISUAL REPORTAGE AND PATTERNS.

WOMEN OF THE SAMBAA ETHNIC GROUP FROM THE USAMBARA MOUNTAINS, NORTHEAST TANZANIA

WWW.LINEOLSSON.COM

617.816.8747   line.olsson@gmail.com

Wall calendar. Daimler / Western Star Trucks

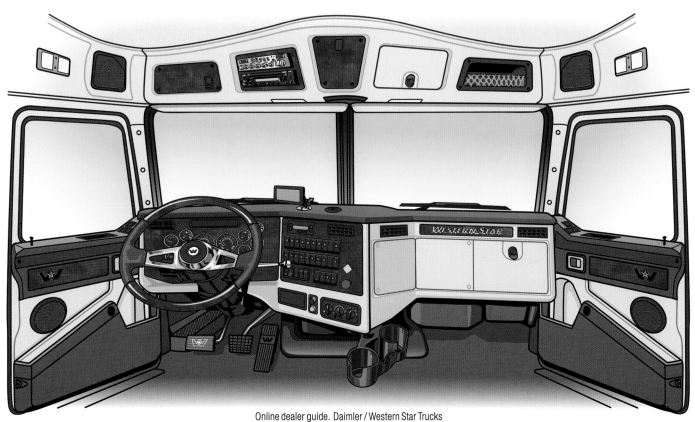

Online dealer guide. Daimler / Western Star Trucks

"Every Day is a Good Day for a Ride" retail print

Editorial. *Flight Training* Magazine

Online dealer guide. Daimler / Western Star Trucks

Collateral piece for grand opening. Oregon Railroad Heritage Museum

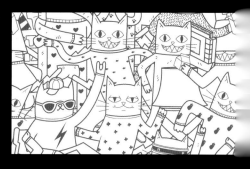

BRYAN HOLLAND | WWW.BRYANHOLLANDARTS.COM | INFO@BRYANHOLLANDARTS.COM | 507-720-4180

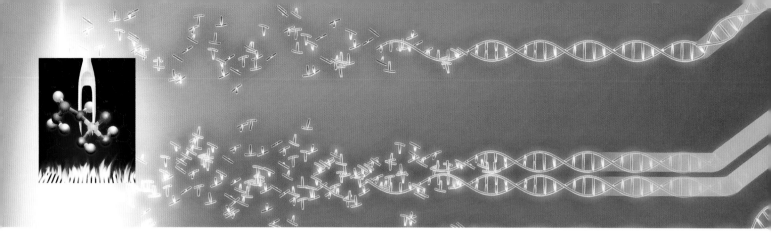

Hemodialysis

Dialysis machine

Blood flows to machine

Filtered blood returned to body

Water Strider - *Gerris remigis*

Middle legs are used for propulsion.

Back legs are used for steering.

Front legs are used for grasping prey.

Science-Art.Com

Where Reality Meets Imagination

Science-Art.Com
Search for Art & Artists

Red Squirrel

Northern Flying Squirrel

Coho Salmon
male above, female below

Chinook Salmon
male

Tentacle

Mouth

Gastrodermis

Stomach

Coenosarc

Mesoglea

Outer Epidermis

Septum

Theca

Basal Plate

Leaf

Stem

Hypocotyl   Cotyledon

Seed coat

Roots

Cathartidae

ELIZABETH LADA Design & Illustration

www.elizabethlada.com   650.279.5211   elizabethlada@gmail.com

Tatjana
Mai-Wyss

tatjanamaiwyss.com

tatjanamaiwyss@hotmail.com

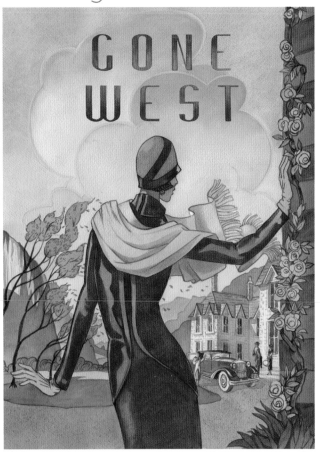

BradleyClarkArt   Retro Illustration

BradleyClarkArt.com   Ph. 646.675.5859   bc@bradleyclarkart.com

PETER GREENWOOD

ILLUSTRATOR

www.peter-greenwood.com

Andrea Fitcha

writer.illustrator@gmail.com
www.andreafitcha.com
503-569-2653

Olmeca Tequila - Global brand icon
Client: Coly Porter Bell. UK

DC Dalgliesh - Retail brand icon
Client: Tayburn. UK

Maryam Tea - Brand crest icon
Client: Good Creative. UK

Naked Turtle Rum - Global brand identity crest
Client: Landor. USA

Crown Royal Whisky - Brand icon
Client: Landor. USA

Glengoyne Whisky - Global brand icon
Client: Good. UK

China Navigation - Identity crest
Client: Zebra Design. Singapore

epicicons
by
CHRIS MITCHELL
ILLUSTRATIVE GLOBAL BRANDS

T +44 (0) 1243 572 099
M +44 (0) 7802 874 349
E chris@epicicons.com
W www.epicicons.com

© All rights reserved on all images

Scott's cod liver oil - Brand identity icon
Client: The Brand Union Singapore for GSK

Courvoisier Napoleon Cognac
Concept brand icon
Client: JKR. UK

The Old Vic - Brand identity icon
Client: Rose. UK

The Old Vic - Brand identity icon
(recrafted for light on dark version)
Client: Rose. UK

Nordlands Pils Beer - Brand icon
Client: Strømme Throndsen Design. Norway

Black Dog Whisky - Global brand icon
Client: Holmes & Marchant. Singapore

epicicons
by
CHRIS MITCHELL
ILLUSTRATIVE GLOBAL BRANDS

T + 44 (0) 1243 572 099
M + 44 (0) 7802 874 349
E chris@epicicons.com
W www.epicicons.com

© All rights reserved on all images

Kenneth McGregor   136 East Main St., Suite 7   330.677.4277   ken@artarmory.com

Rebekah Nichols
www.rebekahnichols.com
(785) 772-1276

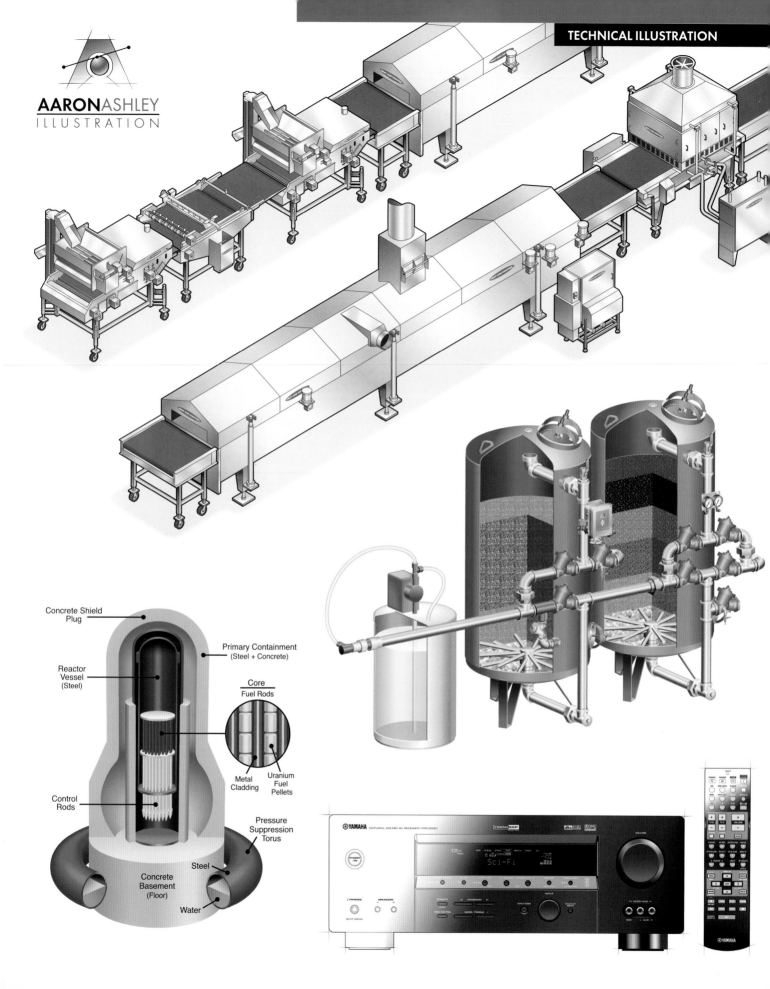

AARONASHLEY
ILLUSTRATION

Concrete Shield
Plug

Primary Containment
(Steel + Concrete)

Reactor
Vessel
(Steel)

Core
Fuel Rods

Control
Rods

Metal
Cladding

Uranium
Fuel
Pellets

Pressure
Suppression
Torus

Steel

Concrete
Basement
(Floor)

Water

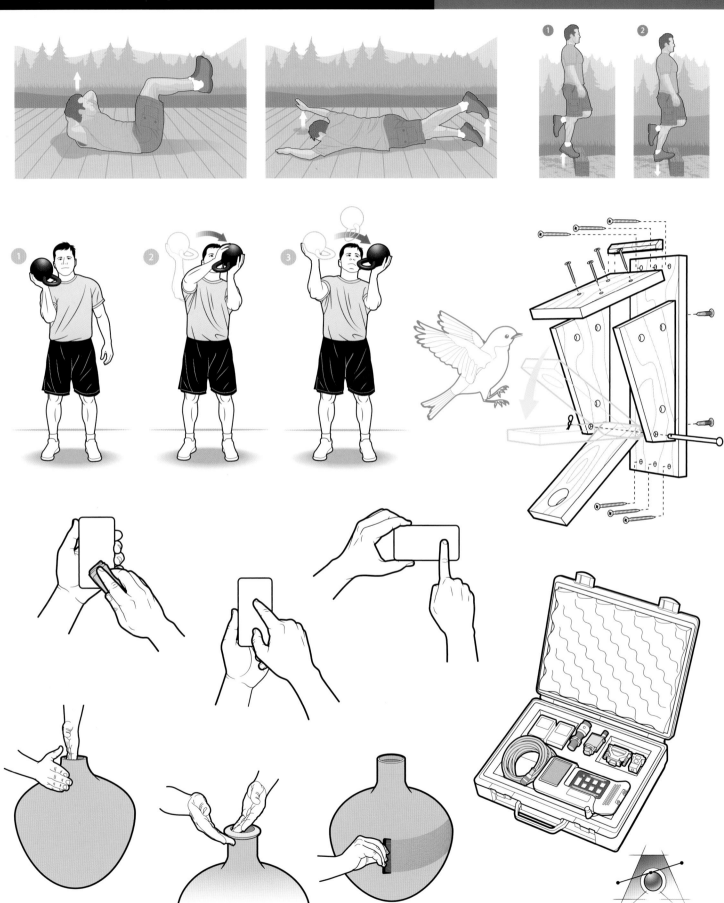

AARONASHLEY
ILLUSTRATION

Amandas
creative studios

Specializing in children and animals

AmandasCreativeStudios.com

adolson75@gmail.com | 765.524.9912 | DirectoryOfIllustration.com/AmandaOlson

TOM JELLETT ILLUSTRATION

www.tomjellett.com

tom@tomjellett.com

TOM JELLETT ILLUSTRATION
www.tomjellett.com
tom@tomjellett.com

www.steveskelton.com

STEVE SKELTON
ILLUSTRATION
ANIMATION
WHITEBOARD

720-652-9777

skelton@frii.com

510

Graham
Franciose

grahamfranciose.com   (860)-869-4637   franciose@gmail.com

erika steiskal
ILLUSTRATION

erikasteiskal.com   erikasteiskal@gmail.com   330.718.1283

KEINYO WHITE

WWW.KEINYOWHITE.COM
KEINYO@KEINYOWHITE.COM
USA: 202 387 6367
INTL: +64 21 081 955 80

Ashley Percival

www.ashleypercival.com

annemarieperks

The Silkie, watercolour and acryl gouache on strathmore bristol board
audio book cover, written by Sandra Horn, Clucket Press

www.annemarieperks.com ~ justanillustrator@me.com ~ +44 1494 775416

ALLEN GARNS
ILLUSTRATION
480 854 3121 · allengarns.com
allen@allengarns.com

Tomb Robber

Friend Magazine

Coming to America

ALLEN GARNS
ILLUSTRATION
480 854 3121 · allengarns.com
allen@allengarns.com

Tombrobber

POLLACK

Illustration ®

607*592*6225
www.AlanPollack.com
apollackstudios@zoom-dsl.com

Alan Wade

www.alanwadeillustration.com   Tel 203 543 5343   email alanwade@mac.com

Publishing   ·   Advertising   ·   Character development   ·   Storyboards

YANA BEYLINSON

ASIAN GINGER
& APPLE
highly fragranced candle

BAMBOO
& JASMINE
highly fragranced candle

HINOKI
BONSAI
highly fragranced candle

COTTON
BLOSSOM
highly fragranced candle

VANILLA
RUM BRÛLÉE
highly fragranced candle

WATERFALL
MIST
highly fragranced candle

CHESAPEAKE BAY CANDLE®

YANA BEYLINSON

Naked Eye Images   New York   516.808.1118   karenchandler.fineartstudioonline.com/collections/68646

Karen Chandler

New York

516.808.1118

karenchandlerfineart.com

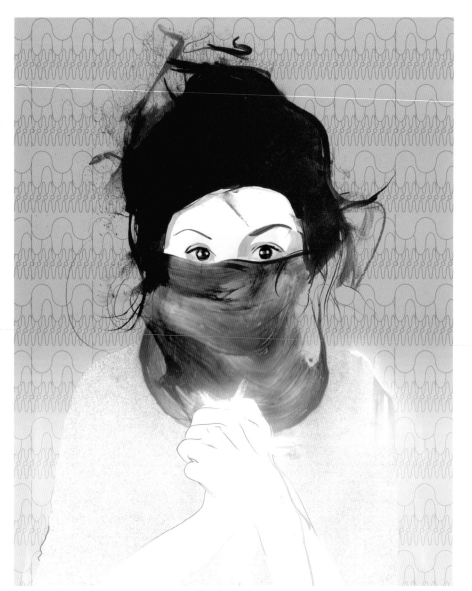

CALEB SIMMONS

www.calebsimmons.co.uk   shout@calebsimmons.co.uk   +44 (0) 7920 408 562

Kristen A. Girard

www.girardillustration.com - 518-796-5759 - kristen@girardillustration.com

Matthew Holmes · Artist
4760 American River Drive
Carmichael, CA 95608

916-971-4727
matthewholmes@att.net

916-971-4727
matthewholmes@att.net

Matthew Holmes · Artist
4760 American River Drive
Carmichael, CA 95608

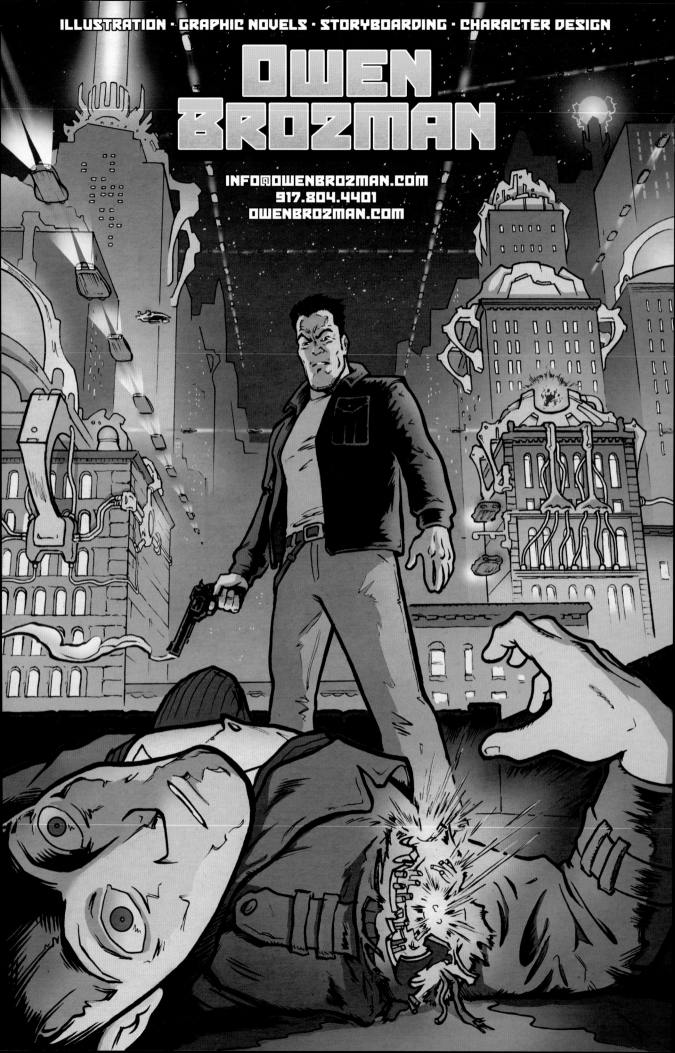

Deborah Lanino

(310) 850-3835
deborahlanino@yahoo.com
www.deborahlanino.com

Scott J. Fowler
(646) 752-2528
ActingOutDesign.com

The Art of Learning

MoMA.org

JPMorganChase

The EARTH is HEATING UP

Let's COOL IT

Gretchen Géser (pronounced Gazer)

Children's Books ("One Bright Ring," Holt, 2013) and illustrations for adults
I work in both traditional and digital media (especially Photoshop and Illustrator) and submit digital files.

518.439.4348 • gretchen.geser@gmail.com • gretchengeser.com • onebrightring.com

games • toys • books • magazines • editorial • 3-D illustrations

comics • advertising • posters • games • toys • books • magazines

Jason Robinson

561-330-8518 / robinzson@aol.com
www.illustration-by-design.com

illustration by design

ryanetterillustration.com **816.373.0586** info@ryanetterillustration.com

ryanetterillustration.com **816.373.0586** info@ryanetterillustration.com

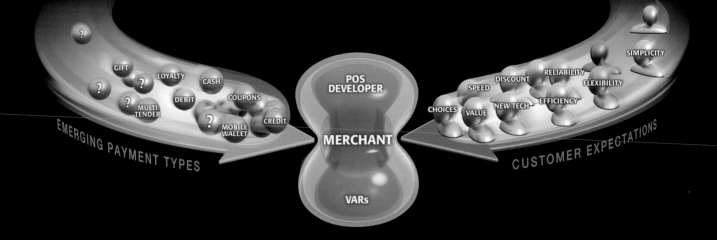

NEW PRODUCT INTRODUCTIONS

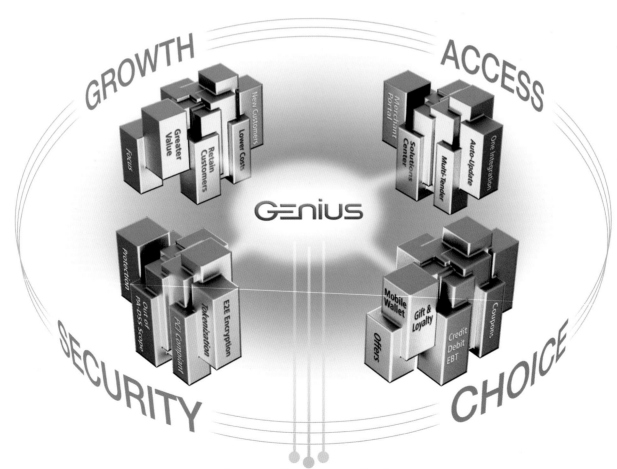

Customer Engagement Device

RON MCPHERSON

www.ronmcpherson.com   310.365.4616   RON.MCP@5ATD.NET

keith skeen

kskeen1@frontier.com   608.220.6145   kskeen.com

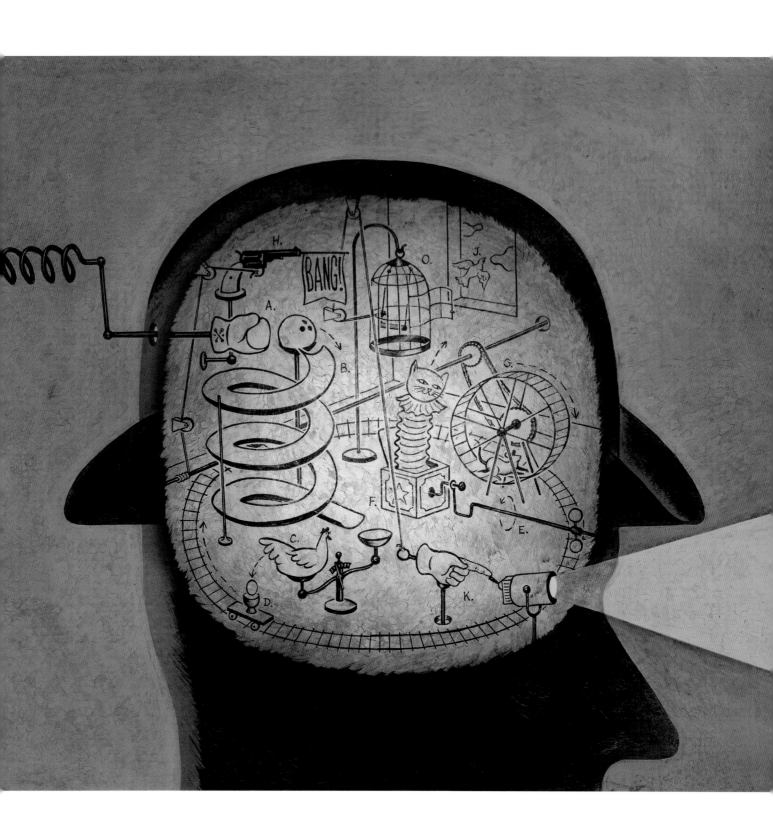

keith skeen

kskeen1@frontier.com   608.220.6145   kskeen.com

Ipsywonger

Ipsywonger **1**

Molegger Gump

Molegger Gump **2**

Finkleglooper

Finkleglooper **3**

Werewimple

Werewimple **4**

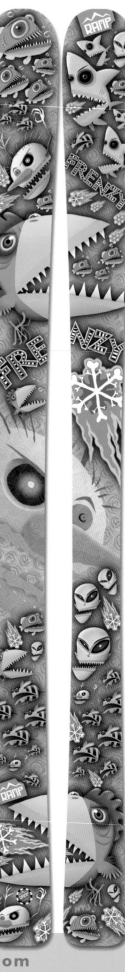

Nathan Y. Jarvis

CONTACT

www.nathanjarvis.com
801-831-0406 nathan@nathanjarvis.com

Beccy Blake

www.beccyblake.com
beccs@beccyblake.com
+44 (0) 7810170542
+44 (0) 1588 640632

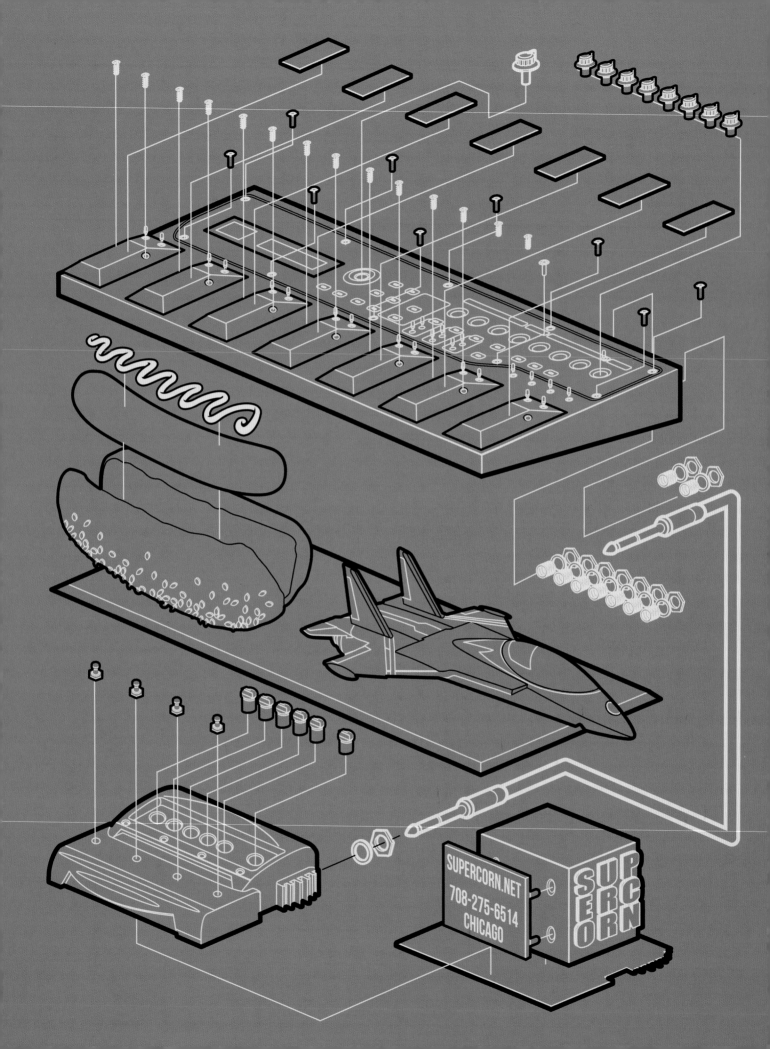

SUPERCORN.NET
708-275-6514
CHICAGO

SUP
ERC
ORN

jill newton

CHILDREN'S BOOKS • EDITORIAL

Clients include:
Bloomsbury
Crocodile Creek
Egmont
HarperCollins
Jellycat
Lion
Orchard
Pearson
Scholastic

t: +44 (0) 7802 761993   e: jillenewt@gmail.com   www.jillnewton.co.uk

Liza Fenech

LizaFenech.com
Liza.Fenech@gmail.com
(443) 745-5422

William Rieser
illustration & design
415-389-0332
WilliamRieser.com

William Rieser

illustration & design

415-389-0332
WilliamRieser.com

PLAY FEARLESS

We're Changing Everything | TropLV.com

James Horvath illustration

www.jamestoons.com
james@jamestoons.com

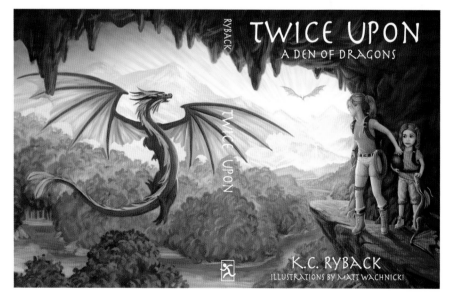

Matt Wachnicki

mattwachnicki@gmail.com

www.mattwachnicki.com

Gavin Ball

Full Circle CS inc.

illustration
visual development
character design
interactive

416 939 4298
gball@full0.com

www.full0.com

NICOLE KAUFMAN ILLUSTRATION

nicolekaufman.com

707 843 1150

happy clients:

barnes + noble
chronicle books
clarkson potter
crown publishers
ddb worldwide
foote, cone + belding
glamour magazine
harper collins
knopf publishing
merck pharmaceuticals
oprah magazine
parenting magazine
random house
reader's digest
tyndale house publishers
weldon owen publishing
williams-sonoma
william morrow
workman publishing

S. ROSS BROWNE

Artist

SRossBrowne.com

804 564 6852

srossbrowne@gmail.com

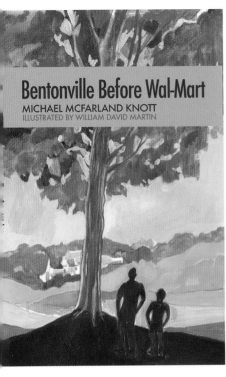

Bentonville Before Wal-Mart

MICHAEL MCFARLAND KNOTT
ILLUSTRATED BY WILLIAM DAVID MARTIN

William D Martin ■ 973-270-6603 ■ www.wdmdesigns.com

funny·people

funny·kids

funny·dogs

funny·money

john@jcolquhoun.com

funny·bands

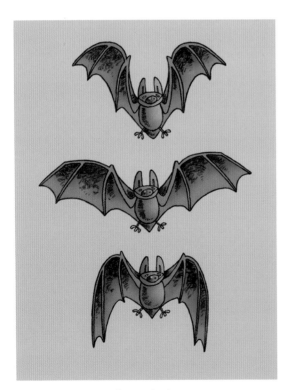

funny·bats

John Colquhoun
funny·stuff
914·217·8805

www.jColquhoun.com

lightspeed
commercial arts

Michael J. Hamers · 7259 Mt. Sherman Road · Niwot, Colorado 80503
Design for Print & Web · Logo Design & Branding · Technical & Product Art
Cell 303-527-1222 · mike@lightspeedca.net · www.lightspeedca.net

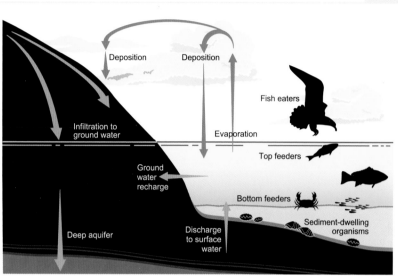

Deposition · Deposition

Fish eaters

Infiltration to ground water

Evaporation

Top feeders

Ground water recharge

Bottom feeders

Sediment-dwelling organisms

Deep aquifer

Discharge to surface water

Nanoparticles are introduced into the water system through interaction with oil, chemicals, sunscreens and more.

**Manufacturing · Technology · Nature · Conceptual
Biomedical Devices · Nanoscience · Oil & Gas Industry**

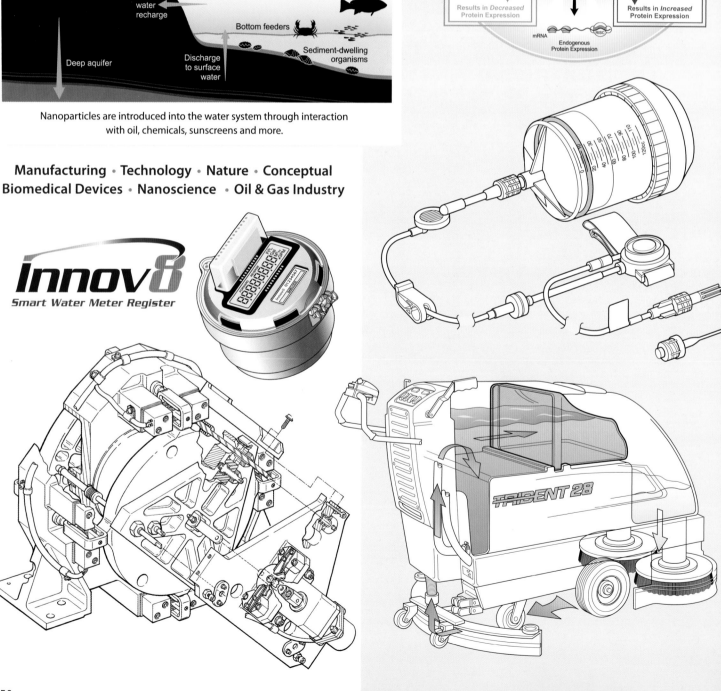

Innov8
Smart Water Meter Register

lightspeed
commercial arts

Michael J. Hamers · 7259 Mt. Sherman Road · Niwot, Colorado 80503
Design for Print & Web · Logo Design & Branding · Technical & Product Art
Cell 303-527-1222 · mike@lightspeedca.net · www.lightspeedca.net

Winner of 20+ national & intenational *awards of excellence* for logo design

The Planet Shifters Network™
ON-DEMAND MEDIA
Helping Conscious Businessess Be Seen and Heard

Turn 2 WORDS MONEY™
Transforming Ideas Into Results

Microgravity™
ENTERPRISES, INC.

Innovative therapies
targeting heart muscle disease
Myogen™

STEVE HENRY
The Web Fellow™
Savvy websites for small business

APEX CRYOTHERAPY

Sweet greens™
Deliciously Healthy Treats

BODY AS™ DOCTOR
by Wayne Garland

Boss WEAR™
The Work Pants That Actually Work!

Genesis™
ACCOUNTING

557

503 320 1207 ✉ jeff_artstuff@me.com jefffoster.com

503 320 1207 ✉ jeff_artstuff@me.com jefffoster.com

AKYU
D E S I G N

3D graphics that inform and illuminate

713.468.9595 (studio)   713.392.3628 (mobile)   questell@akyudesign.com   www.akyudesign.com

Adam Questell

A KYU DESIGN

3D graphics that inform and illuminate

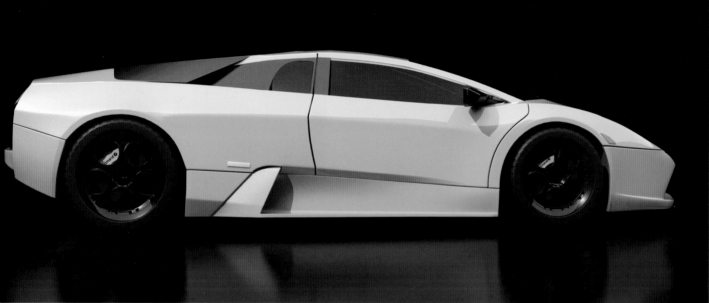

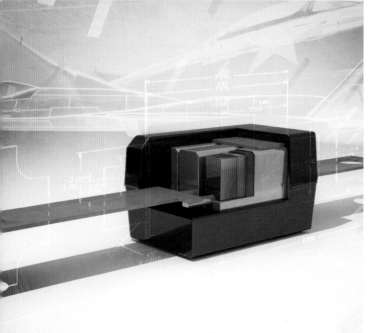

Adam Questell questell@akyudesign.com 713.468.9595 (studio) 713.392.3628 (mobile) akyudesign.com

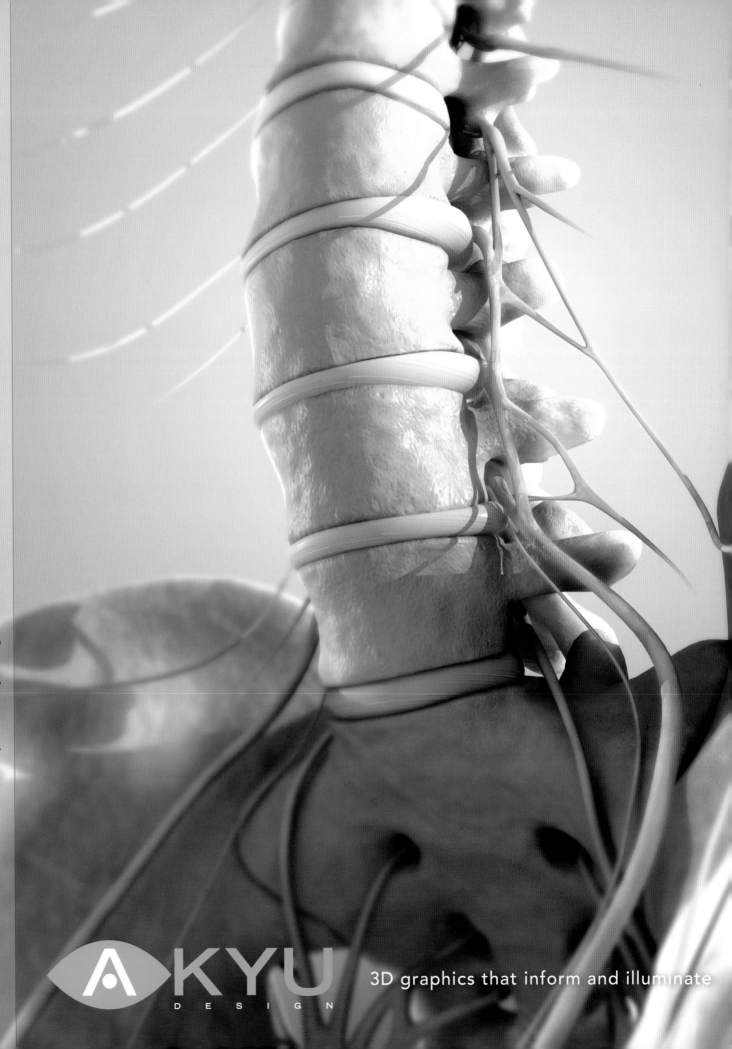

Adam Questell

questell@akyudesign.com

713.468.9595 (studio) 713.392.3628 (mobile)

akyudesign.com

AKYU
DESIGN

3D graphics that inform and illuminate

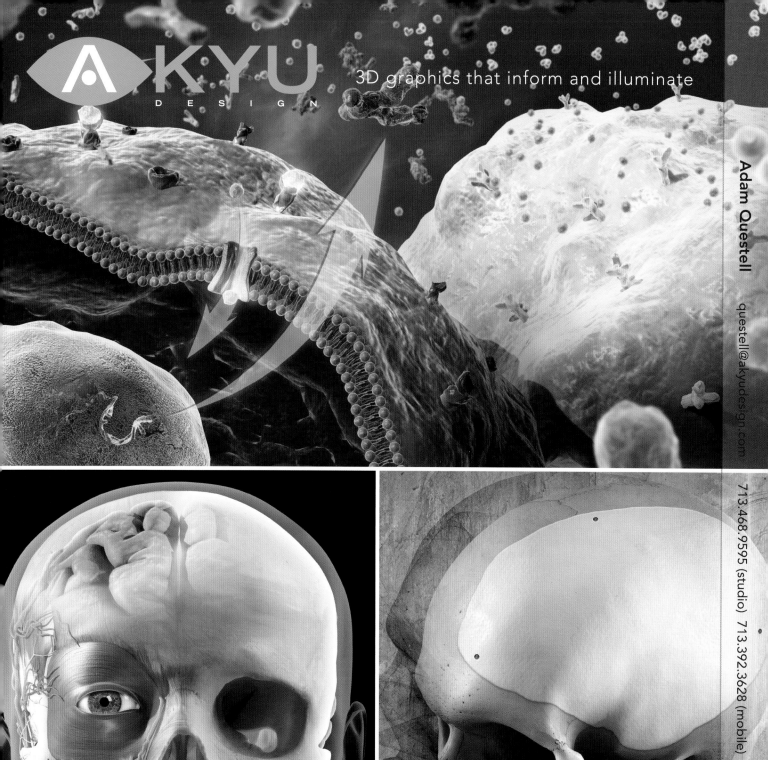

AKYU
DESIGN

3D graphics that inform and illuminate

Adam Questell

questell@akyudesign.com

713.468.9595 (studio) 713.392.3628 (mobile)   akyudesign.com

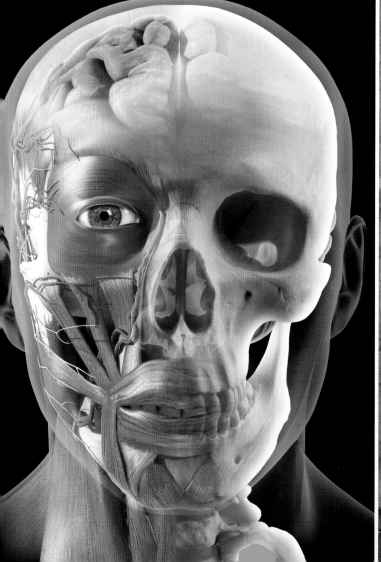

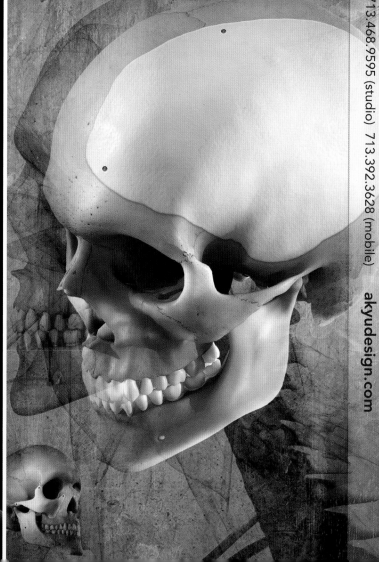

jason lethcoe
old world woodcuts
jasonlethcoe@mac.com

WWW.
woodcutart.
blogspot.com

410-371-4814
www.SQSchwartz.com
SQSchwartz@Gmail.com

Richard Beacham +44 7771963980

mail@richardbeacham.co.uk

www.richardbeacham.co.uk

Rosemary McGuirk

rosemarym@tds.net • rosemarymcguirk.com
P.O. Box 202 Elkins, NH 03233 USA
(603) 748-2115

paper collage

JESSICA GONZALEZ
ILLUSTRATION + DESIGN + ART DIRECTION

WEB :: www.jessicaspitsfire.com

TEL :: 678.763.7431

MAIL :: me@jessicaspitsfire.com

in /jessicaspitsfire

DON DYEN
215 968 9083
d.dyen@verizon.net

Client: Virginia Shakespeare Festival, 2014

PAULA GOODMAN KOZ

phone: 757.253.8950 email: vitabreve@cox.net visit: paulagoodmankoz.com

PARLIAMENT OF OWLS

Client: Bryn Mawr College Alumnae Committee, Class of 1969

PAULA GOODMAN KOZ

phone: 757.253.8950   email: vitabreve@cox.net   visit: paulagoodmankoz.com

www.janmartin.co.uk
jan@janmartin.co.uk

susan@abovo.net

517.545.5000 | Abovo | abovo.net

Jono
Doiron

illustrator

www.jonodoiron.com

jono@jonodoiron.com

+1.438.822.8644

D
IS FOR
OINO

PAMELA ROUZER
illustration + design

949.310.3665 | PAMROUZER@GMAIL.COM | PAMELAROUZER.COM

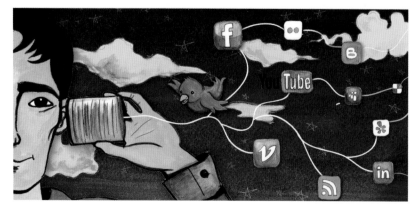

paul lachine
illustrations

519.351.8711

plachine@paullachine.com   www.paullachine.com

576

DANIEL SEEX

WWW.THEJOYOFSEEX.CO.UK

© +44 791 333 6434 ✉ DANIEL_SEEX@HOTMAIL.CO.UK

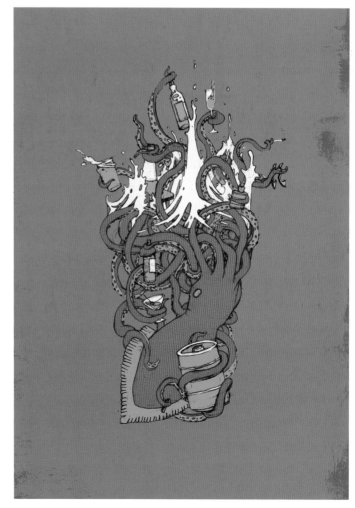

BETSY WALLIN ILLUSTRATION - betsywallin@gmail.com - www.betsywallin.com

tom foty

fotyartinc

steve@munrocampagna.com   312-335-8925

munrocampagna.com/illustration/foty_tom/portfolio.htm

Monica V. Loncola

ILLUSTRATION & FINE ART

USA 415-250-8544 • monica@monicaloncola.com • monicaloncola.com • monicaloncola.faso.com

adidas

originals

EDDIEGUY.NET | 201.251.7660 | EMAIL ME AT: EDDIE.GUY@VERIZON.NET

JAMES SANDIFER
• Illustration • Animation •
www.jimsandifer.co.uk

james.w.sandifer@gmail.com

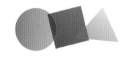

+44 (0) 77955 943 87

www.alessandradivizia.com
001 (917) 678 2080   ad@alessandradivizia.com

BUSY

NEVER! YES

teeleedesign.com
teelee@me.com
+44 161 484 5995

ZINASAUNDERS PAINTING | GRAPHIC | ANIMATION

WWW.ZINASAUNDERS.COM   212.777.1201   ZINA@ZINASAUNDERS.COM

Mario Lord

What can I draw for you?

www.thedrawinglord.com

TheDrawingLord@gmail.com

Skype: lord_of_the_dring

WILD WINGS

BIRDS of PREY

RYU
CREATIVE
DIGITAL PHOTO
COMPOSITING

BOOK COVERS | CD ART
3D WORK | DIGITAL ART

www.**ryucreative**.co.uk

A 3D VR

MONSTERS
THE DEEP

DIVE IN! THIS BOOK CONTAINS
LIVE CREATURES

BOOK SPREADS DESIGNED BY **RYUNEO DESIGNS**

"Maxell 10pk"
Ron Gill
Gilosan.com
201.696.6800

DAVID HELFREY

T 503.705.0104 • **E** DAVE@DAVEHELFREY.COM • **W** DAVEHELFREY.COM

©2014 David Helfrey • © Atmel Corp. • © Idle Games • © Seattle Business

carol way wood

508.843.2250
cwaywood@hotmail.com
www.carolwaywood.com

A Fine Book of Letters

An Illuminated Journey through the Alphabet

Carol Way Wood

One Should Treat All Creatures in The World As One Would Like to Be Treated

– Mahavira, Sutrakritanga

(((SiriusXM)))
CHANNEL 127

SUSAN ABRAMS
412.521.1743
abrdes@verizon.net

TYPOGRAPHY
IDENTITY & BRANDING
GRAPHIC DESIGN

Blog: chucktoddartist.wordpress.com   Twitter: @ChuckToddartist   LinkedIn: www.linkedin.com/in/chucktoddillustration

visual journalism   **illustration**   infographics

Lowell Fulson
West Coast blues legend

Billie Holiday
Performed at the Lincoln Theatre

Aretha Franklin
and other legends performed on 7th Street

Bob Geddins
"The Godfather of Oakland Blues," and Big Town records

www.chucktodd.net   chucktoddartist@gmail.com   925 818-7365

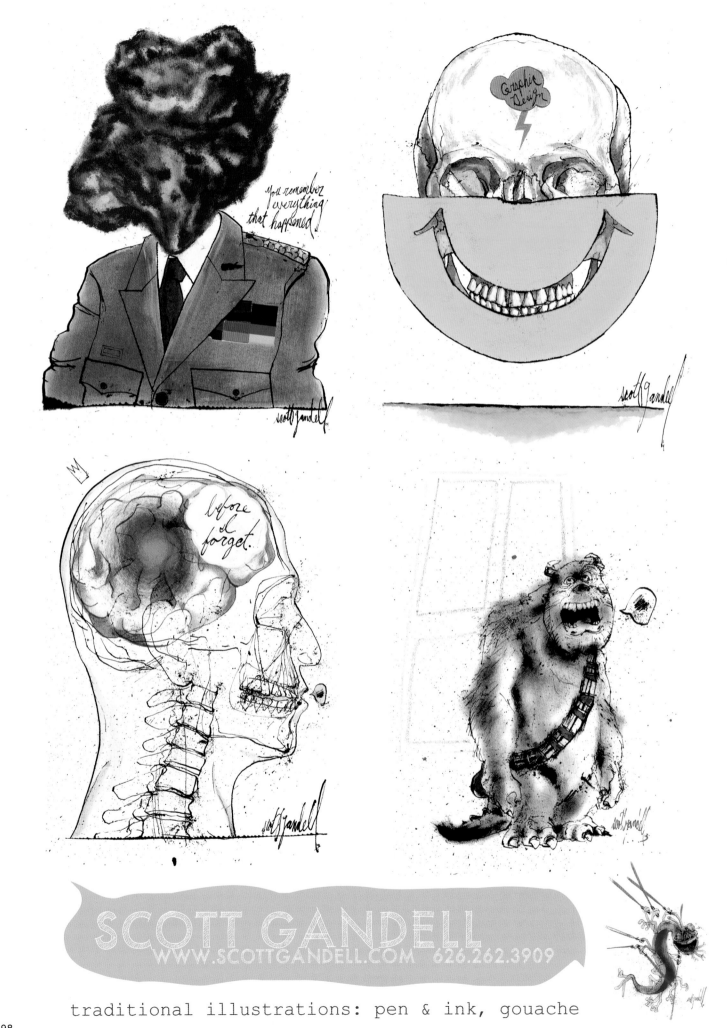

traditional illustrations: pen & ink, gouache

Peter Cook
illustrationist.ca
(416) 463-3315
peter@illustrationist.ca

t peterlcook.tumblr.com
@DoodlePeter

Medtronic M___ Comics Walmart Mattel Scientific American Lego
Dell Computer Houghton Mifflin Scholastic McDonalds PC Magazine
Warner Brothers Wall Street Journal K'nex Toys Wired Magazine IBM
Fisher-Price Boy Scouts of America Chicago White Sox Goodyear Atari
Zebco Brunswick Christianity Today Pizza Hut Tyson Nike McGraw Hill

918•342•3048
www.miraclestudios. com
miracle@miraclestudios.com

Tom Helland
Design + Illustration

602

tomhelland.com
248-202-0096

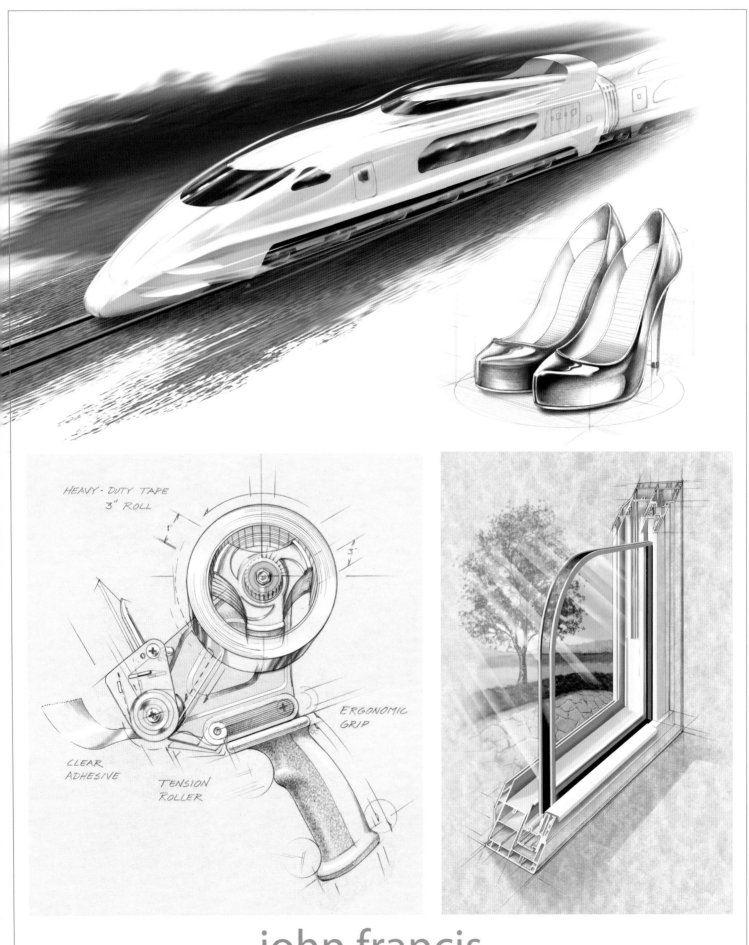

HEAVY - DUTY TAPE
3" ROLL

ERGONOMIC
GRIP

CLEAR
ADHESIVE

TENSION
ROLLER

john francis
industrialillustrator.com   303.880.7770

MICHAEL HOEWELER

p 513 703 7957   *e* michaelhoeweler@gmail.com   *w* www.michaelhoeweler.com

p   513 703 7957   *e*   michaelhoeweler@gmail.com   *w*   www.michaelhoeweler.com

Paul Hostetler Illustration

Paul Hostetler Illustration   (912) 713-6127   www.phostetler.com

606

BARBARA SPURLL 1·800·989·3123 WWW.BARBARASPURLL.COM

DAVID PLUNKERT

VISIT: DAVIDPLUNKERT.COM   PHONE: 410 235 7803   TWITTER: @PLUNKERT

IMAGE ORIGINALLY CREATED FOR SAWKILL LUMBER CO.

JOYCE HESSELBERTH

VISIT: **JOYCEHESSELBERTH.COM**　　PHONE: **410 235 7803**　　TWITTER: **@HESSELBERTH**

IMAGE ORIGINALLY CREATED FOR GUNPOWDER RIVER ARTFEST

anna goodson
illustration agency
info@agoodson.com
www.agoodson.com
+ 1 514.482.0488 T
+ 1 514.482.0686 F

paul blow

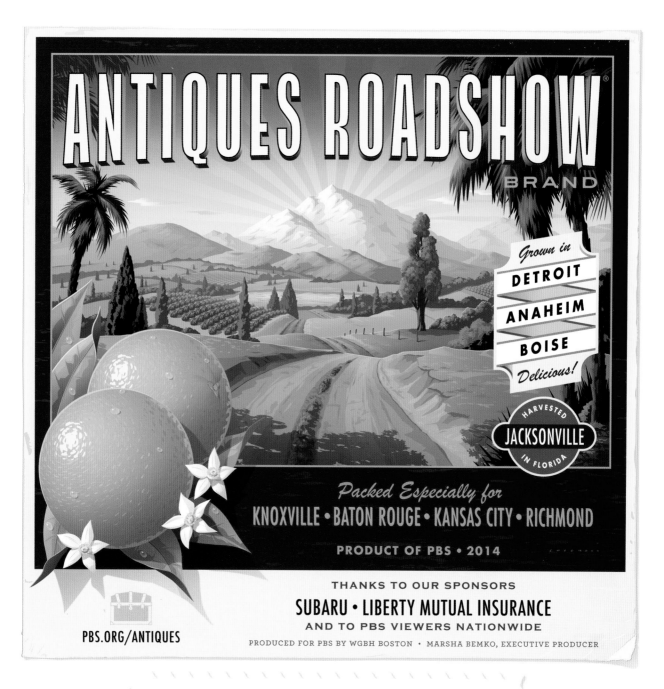

DAN COSGROVE | cosgrovedesign.com | 312.765.8911

312.765.8911 | cosgrovedesign.com   DAN COSGROVE

BRYAN FYFFE

WWW.BRYANFYFFE.COM · BFYFFE@GMAIL.COM · 507-358-1937

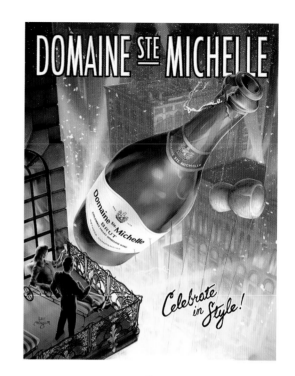

WWW.LEEMOYER.COM

971 · 533 · 0500

LEE@LEEMOYER.COM

THE LITTLE MERMAID

CLASSIC ILLUSTRATION FOR PRODUCT AND ENTERTAINMENT

www.jasminguerardalie.ca
514 793-3235

618

COMICS, ANIMATION, APPS, CHARACTER DESIGN, STORYBOARDS - YOTZSTUDIOS.COM (918) 639-3729

ONCE *THE ELECTROFIER* SEIZED CONTROL OF THE ANCIENT GOLEM THEY KNEW ALL WAS *LOST!*

See the Animation!

STUDIOS

Saffron Pears Poached in Wine

ANZA BRANCH LIBRARY

Venezia

Cindy Salans Rosenheim
415. 244. 2513

RAILWAY STATION
Mori & Bozzi
GRAND CANAL
S. ROCCO · FRARI
S. PANTALON
S. Giovanna
RIALTO
Santa Margherita · Masks
Ponte dei Pugni
S. Barnaba
Friulana
Toletto · Gondola Yard
ACCADEMIA
S. Barbaro
SALUTE · PUNTA DELLA DOGANA
Marina & Susanna Sent